# Devil Wind
# Fire Wagons

# Devil Wind Fire Wagons

Celebrating the 75th Anniversary of
The Los Angeles County Forester and Fire Warden Department
now known as
The Los Angeles County Fire Department

(July 1, 1920–July 1, 1995)

## David Boucher

*Very best wishes to Gordon Pearson
from a fellow member of Class #23 —
the cream of the crop! Regards,*

*David Boucher*

Carter–Grove Publishers
Costa Mesa

Boucher, David, 1936–
    Devil wind fire wagons : history of Los Angeles county fire
department apparatus, 1920–1995 / David Boucher.
        p.      cm.
    Includes index.
    LCCN: 96–85544
    ISBN 0–9625946–5–2
    1. Fire departments—California—Equipment and supplies—
History.   2. Los Angeles County (Calif.). Fire Dept.—
Equipment and supplies—History—20th century.   I Title.
TH9505.L808B68   1996          628.9'25'0979493
                               QBI96–40091

*Editor-in-Chief*: R. Dale Magee

*Finish Typing and Secondary Editing*: Terri O'Hanlon

**Photo and Apparatus Data Credits**
The following persons are held in deep appreciation by the author for their material assistance in locating and supplying photographs or technical data appearing in this book. No one person can possess all the knowledge necessary to assemble a work such as this. Hopefully, with the publication of this book, we will have come a little closer to the goal.

    Special thanks to Chiefs Sherrill and Hoffman of the Los Angeles County Fire Department Public Information Office for once again consenting to allow the use of dozens of photographs taken in the 1930's through 60's by department staff photographers. Some of these photos also appeared in my first book, *Ride the Devil Wind* (Fire Publications Inc., 1991). It was necessary to reuse those photos because they were the only ones known to the author, some of them being quite rare.

    Hopefully no one has been overlooked in preparing this list.

| | | | |
|---|---|---|---|
| Glen Alton | "Dot and Larry" | Charles Madderom | Shaun Ryan |
| Larry Arnold | Tom Estlow | R. Dale Magee | Hiram Swallow |
| George "Smokey" Bass | Keith Gustavson | Jerry Meehan | James Turner |
| Alan Boucher | William Hattersly | Kenneth Morris | |
| Des Barton | Rick Harp | Arnold Muench | and the Hall of |
| Chris Cavette | Robert Hewitt | John Nieto | Flame Museum in |
| Ray Chambers | Kenneth Jury | James Page | Phoenix, Arizona |
| Donald Croucher | Keith Klinger | Roland Percey | |
| Larry Cummings | Matthew Lee | Walt Pittman | |

Special thanks also to Division Chief Fred Boehm and Craig Lindberg of the Fire Fleet Services Section of the Services Bureau for supplying computer readouts for apparatus purchased since 1988.

# A Dedication

In searching for a person to whom to dedicate my first book, *Ride the Devil Wind*, it was relatively simple to choose Captain John Whelan, for he was as close to being the Department Historian as could be found during the 1940's and 50's. He, along with Carol Jorgensen during the 60's and 70's, carefully recorded, researched, and hoarded drawers and boxes full of irreplaceable written information and photographs. In choosing a person for this second book, it was also fairly simple for me.

Robert Dale Magee is a well-known "fire buff," fire historian, author, lecturer. and fountain of information on fire apparatus from the 'teens through the 50's. He is also, thankfully, a personal friend of mine, and has been since 1972 when he was my teacher in a Chemistry for Firemen course at Pasadena City College. Again thankfully, he agreed to edit *Ride the Devil Wind*, and in so doing assisted this author immensely by thoroughly sanitizing my efforts. He taught me word economy and helped me become better at this craft. I am very grateful to him.

Dale is a pioneer among fire historians. He was a charter member of the Box 15 Club of Los Angeles and originator of the "Fire Fan Register," a long-time member of SPAAMFAA, a former photographer for the *Los Angeles Times*, and author of two books, *Chemistry for Firemen* and *A History of Los Angeles City Fire Apparatus*. He taught chemistry at the high school level in the La Canada and Pasadena school systems, and numerous fire science classes at Pasadena City College. His collection of fire apparatus photographs is peerless, and supplied many an old photograph for this book.

# Table of Contents

# Foreword

With the exception of well-trained fire fighters, nothing in the Fire Service is of more importance than well-designed and perfectly functioning fire apparatus. From the earliest hand drawn and operated pumpers of Benjamin Franklin's day to the modern fire equipment of today, the "Enjine" has been of prime significance in the Fire Service.

When compared to fire departments throughout the United States, the Los Angeles County Fire Department is considered to be fairly young. Having been formed by the combining of two organizations, the Los Angeles County Forester and Fire Warden Department (established in 1920) and the Los Angeles County Fire Protection Districts (established in 1923–25), with an ever-increasing number of "contract cities" joining in, a wide variety of fire apparatus has resulted.

In the beginning, two distinctly different types of fire equipment were in service. The Forester and Fire Warden apparatus was designed primarily for fighting wildland fires. The district areas, known as "flatlands," were designed for fires of structures, grass, rubbish, vehicles, bridges, and oil derricks, which included petroleum refineries and tank farms.

This book illustrates all primary types of fire apparatus utilized by the Los Angeles County Fire Department over the seventy-five year span of time from 1920 to 1995.

Over the past three-quarters of a century, the Los Angeles County Fire Department has grown into the third largest department in the United States in terms of numbers of fire stations, fire apparatus, and related rolling stock.

*Dale Magee photo*

# Introduction

It is fascinating to note that the "last word in fire apparatus" of the 1920's and 30's would be considered, by today's standards, totally deficient. Yet, somehow, these old rigs got the job done!

The older apparatus took a little longer to arrive at the fire scene (sometimes breaking down en route), did not carry as much equipment or pump as much water, and did not have radio equipment; but *did* often bring more manpower to the fire scene than we are used to seeing today. Effective work *was* accomplished "on scene."

Although this book is primarily about the development of fire apparatus of the County of Los Angeles, it is the innate devotion to service by fire fighters both past and present that really make it work! The photographs in this book frequently (and intentionally) show fire apparatus without personnel only because the fire apparatus purist prefers it that way.

The Los Angeles County Fire Department provides protection services truly from the desert to the sea, including the mountains, valleys, flatlands and coastlines of the many communities in between.

While he was Chief Engineer of the organization, Keith Klinger used to say, "There really is no Los Angeles County Fire Department as such." And there was always a twinkle in his eyes when he said it. He liked to refer to the Department as the "Los Angeles *Country* Fire Department" a reference to the ofttimes rural setting of its theatre of operations.

Fire apparatus serving the Los Angeles County communities of the 1920's and 30's would most certainly be considered deficient by today's standards. In many areas, very long response patterns were the norm.

Imagine the entire area of West Hollywood of today being serviced by two 1924 750 gallon per minute (G.P.M.) Type 12 American La France triples, each with a three-man crew, plus, if available, one or two call men. Not so many years ago this was the norm.

This book depicts the Los Angeles County Fire Department's history and progress relative to its fire apparatus, providing protection for its citizens over a 75-year span of time.

# Earliest Forestry and Volunteer Apparatus 1920-1936

I

With the assignment of the responsibility for fire protection in Los Angeles County territory to the Forestry and Fish and Game Department on July 1, 1920, Forester Stewart H. Flintham became the closest to being a genuine "Fire Chief" yet seen for the unincorporated areas. The volunteer system, heretofore utilized by Fire Warden W. B. Morgan, was *only* that. It possessed no mobile apparatus for a chief to utilize or direct. Hand-operated tools such as shovels, rakes, and wet gunny sacks utilized by volunteer wardens and/or the general public were all they had to work with.

Forester Flintham realized at an early date that some sort of mobile fire equipment was needed for general fire fighting. He proceeded to have neighborhoods canvassed by local volunteer wardens in

This 1936 photo shows Forestry Personnel about to move out for the annual pre-fire planning overnight excursion. Note pack mules extreme left and right.

*John Whelan collection*

In this 1929 photo, Chief Assistant Forester Joseph Davis shows off transportation used to access lookout towers, perform Fish & Game & Fire Patrol and generally access the back country of Los Angeles County.

*Des Barton photo*

order to collect money for trailers. When and where enough funds were collected, a district was formed, within which trailers could be used.

Twelve identical fire trailers were built for districts scattered throughout the county. Two of the trailers were initially unassigned.

Each trailer was designed to be towed by any vehicle capable of doing so, and was parked in a private garage or suitable central location within the purchasing district.

Training was provided in the use of the equipment placed in each trailer. Persons receiving such training were called upon to tow the fire trailer to the fire scene. This was dependent upon the volunteers' availability and willingness to do so.

During the few years just prior to 1923, several districts did purchase used fire equipment to supplant the trailers. There was a wide variety of equipment

utilized, with each district or area free to choose, and, in many cases, build their own make and style of apparatus. Most of this equipment was either traded in on permanent apparatus between 1923 and 1925, sold outright, or scrapped.

Prior to 1929, fire apparatus utilized by the Los Angeles County Forester and Fire Warden was of makeshift variety. The days of modified tree-watering trucks as part-time fire engines needed to be terminated if the Fire Warden aspect of the Department was to undergo development and professionalization. It was a time for expediency.

Forester Reinmuller was selected to design a new type of tanker/pumper to be specifically utilized for fighting grass and brush fires. It was desired that he custom design this apparatus for use on terrain peculiar to the hills and valleys of Southern California. This apparatus needed to be large

Forester Ole Townsend at the wheel of one of the two 1924 Reo-Obenchain-Boyer District rigs turned back to the Forestry Department due to the inability of the districts to pay for them. Photo taken in 1928 in front of the Verdugo Division H.Q., 2910 W. Michigan (Foothill Blvd.). They were later labeled pumpers "A" & "B".

*W. Noller photo*

This early teens flatbed truck with slip-on tank of perhaps 500 gal. was the precursor of the first tree-watering/fire fighting conversions used by the forester and fire warden. Sadly, truck data is not known.

*L.A. County Forestry photo*

enough and of adequate horsepower in order to fulfill the assigned task of carrying large amounts of 1-1/2 inch hose, miscellaneous hand tools, and an adequate water supply—all of this off paved roads and in hilly country.

The Moreland Truck Company of Burbank, California, was chosen to manufacture most of the units purchased between 1929 and 1936. Chassis sizes ranged from 2 tons to 7-1/2 tons. A suitably sized Hercules engine was chosen as the power plant for each apparatus. Smaller apparatus came with one hose reel for 1-inch cotton-jacketed hose. The larger apparatus had two hose reels. Pneumatic tires were specified to meet the mostly off-pavement driving demands. All these units were assigned the letters "G" through "M" for general identification in addition to the shop identification number. The shop number was always preceded by the letter "N." Pumper "S," for example, carried shop number N-346.

Also purchased during this time was a smaller pumper manufactured by the White Motor Company of Cleveland, Ohio. This 1934 unit was built on a 2-ton chassis (as was its Moreland counterpart). It carried all 1-1/2 inch supply hose and a hose reel holding 300 feet of 1-inch cotton-jacketed hose. A 250 G.P.M. Barton power take-off pump was mounted between the front bumper and the radiator. Designated Pumper "Q", it was originally assigned to the Eaton Canyon Patrol Station (now Fire Station 66). In 1938 it was moved to San Dimas Headquarters Station (now Station 64) as a second engine, and then transferred to the districts in 1939. It was placed in service as the first piece of apparatus for Engine Company 39, located in the Bell Gardens area.

A Singleton Model "B" Mack 350 G.P.M. pumper tanker was purchased in 1932, Pumper "P". This rig was built to the now standard Forester and Fire Warden specifications for major brush fire fighting apparatus. Its original assignment was to the Newhall Station (now Station 73).

These two White dual purpose tree-watering & fire fighting 600 gallon tankers (one a 1925, the other a 1926 model) were later labeled pumpers "C" & "D". Note the 38 G.P.M. Pacific portable pumps supplying the monitors on top of the tanks.

*L.A. Co. Forestry photo, Dale Magee collection*

Sister apparatus, pumpers "E" & "F" showing their fire fighting prowess. These 400 gallon 1926
White tankers were still in reserve in 1948, and were never repainted red.

*L.A. Co. Forestry photo*

The 1916 model horse-
drawn Army field kitchen
unit utilized on rare occasions by the Forester &
Fire Warden.
It was stored at the
Pacoima Warehouse.

*L.A. Co. Forestry photo*

Verdugo Division person-
nel pose on the 1929
Buick pick-up. The tallest
man in the back is
Roland Percey. Walter
Noller on the 1928
Harley-Davidson motor-
cycle. Photo taken in late
1928, just prior to mov-
ing to La Cañada.

*W. Noller photo*

1929–33 saw the delivery
of several pieces of
pumper/tanker
equipment. These units
were designed by
Forester Reinmuller
working with the More-
land Co. of Burbank,
California, and were
labeled pumpers "G"
through "M". Pictured
here is pumper "K" at
the Pine Canyon Patrol
Station (Station 78).
These units featured 185
H.P. Hercules engines,
300 G.P.M. main pumps,
and 400 gallon water
tanks. Windshields were
added in 1938.

*Dale Magee collection*

Senior Fire Warden Roland Percey, center, observes his crew pumping through two 1-1/2" and one 1" hose lines on Meadow Grove near the new Arroyo Seco Division H.Q. (now F.S. 82). Pumper "G" here is newly in service this summer of 1930. Note that the overhead ladder rack has yet to be installed.

*W. Noller photo*

A profile photo of Pumper "J" assigned to the Soledad H.Q. station in Newhall. This 1930 pumper/tanker is equipped with a 14' roof ladder only.

*Carson photo*

The business end of three 1929 Buick convertible pickup trucks upon completion of their custom building in the Mission St. shops. One was assigned to each of three Forestry Division Headquarters for use by the Senior Warden in charge.

*L.A. Co. Forestry photo by Arnold Muench*

Forestry Fire Warden & Fish & Game Patrolman "Bill" Williams astride his early 1930's Harley-Davidson, #211. From 1927 until the early 1950's, such patrolmen could carry a firearm if they so desired.

*Arnold Muench photo*

This late 1930's Harley Davidson, #217, was among the last delivered to the Forester & Fire Warden. These 2-cylinder workhorses were phased out in favor of the 1/2-ton pickup or "Jeep" patrol unit so that a pump and water tank could be utilized by the patrolman.

*Arnold Muench Photo*

Two good views of the 1932 Moreland pumper/tanker assigned to the San Dimas Division H.Q. station, currently station 64. labeled pumper "M" it was one of the very few engines delivered during the Great Depression. This unit also came with the 185 H.P. Hercules engine, a 300 G.P.M. centrifugal main pump and a 400 gallon tank.

*Carson photos*

Purchased for the newly completed Eaton Canyon Patrol Station, currently Station 66 in Altadena, this 1934 White pumper/tanker sported a front-mount Barton 250 G.P.M. and a 200 gallon water tank. Labeled Pumper "Q", it was a rare Great Depression delivery.

*Arnold Muench photo*

A professionally posed photo of Pumper "P" when first delivered to the Newhall Station, currently station 73. This 1933 Mack Model "B" had a 300 G.P.M. pump and the standard 400 gallon tank, and was the first Mack delivered to the F & FW.

*Unknown photographer*

Rolling stock and personnel assigned to the Arroyo Seco Division H.Q. in La Cañada in 1932. From left, a new Harley Davidson motorcycle patrol, a 1931 White Squad, (small pumper/personnel hauler) a 1929 Moreland 300 G.P.M. pumper with 400 gallon tank, a 1929 Buick command car, (actually a pick-up) and a 1929 Ford Model A patrol truck. Chief Roland Percey, 2nd from right, here in command of the entire Division, turned 94 in May of 1996.

*L.A. Co. Forestry photo*

Chief Forestry Assistant Joe Davis in action with the Forestry Department's communications radio set built onto a Dodge screen truck, circa 1923. The F & FW used radio continuously from that time on.

*L.A. County Forestry photo*

A very rare photograph showing Horse Patrolman Heine Wertz ready to march in a local parade. No doubt the sign and bow tie remained at home while actually on patrol. Circa 1925.

*John Whelan Collection*

This 1925 Buick "pickup," custom built by the Mission St. Shops, responded out of L.A. H.Q. on Lehigh St. Field Division Wardens had similar vehicles by 1929.

*Arnold Muench photo*

Taken in 1925, this photo shows the first cargo truck owned by the F & FW, a 1924 White, at the Lehigh St. warehouse. A good place for the spare would be on the left front wheel, it would appear.

*Arnold Muench Photo*

A 1930 photo showing Forester Barney Paul's steed just prior to beginning an inspection trip up Big Rock Creek to the Mt. Islip lookout. A mixture of horses and automotive vehicles was utilized by the F & FW during this time.

*John Whelan Collection*

The marvelous Pacific Portable Pump, shown here drafting from a canvas cistern, was used extensively by the F & FW from 1930 until WW II. Weighing 75 lbs., it could be carried by two men to any remote location and obtain water from a creek. It pumped a maximum of 38 G.P.M.

*Arnold Muench photo*

Shown here at Malibu H.Q., presently station 65, Pumper "R", the last Moreland purchased for the
F & FW is shown in 1948 with windshield and sealed beam headlights added. Pumper "R"
featured a 300 G.P.M. pump, a 185 H.P. Hercules engine and a 400 gallon tank.

*Dale Magee photo*

Unfortunately partially blocked by Forester Turner, the F &
FW's first tractor, a Caterpillar #30 rakes brush on Sawmill
Mountain. This 1925 photo shows that the bulldozer blade
was not yet on the market.

*Arnold Muench photo*

The Verdugo Division (La Crescenta) was assigned this
"Ambulance Car" in 1928 for transporting "injured" mem-
bers of the Department. George Taylor in the side car and
Walter Noller on the Harley-Davidson pose in front of
pumper "B" in the temporary quarters on Michigan Ave.
(Foothill Blvd.)

*Walter Noller photo*

# II Earliest Fire District Apparatus 1920-1931

With the formation of the first Los Angeles County Fire Protection Districts during the years 1923–25, the need arose for the purchase of fire apparatus for those districts that could afford it. The equipment used by the volunteers during the previous years had been inadequate for the task at hand. Therefore, the decision was made to ask for bidding on heavier, sturdier equipment with larger pump capacities.

Three firms were awarded contracts for a total of 29 triple combination pumpers: American La France and Foamite Company of Elmira, New York; the Stutz Fire Engine Company of Indianapolis, Indiana; and the REO Company of Lansing, Michigan.

American La France delivered sixteen Type 75 750 G.P.M. pumpers in 1924. The Stutz Company delivered six Type K-3 450 G.P.M. pumpers, and the REO Company delivered seven 350 G.P.M. pumpers. All apparatus was delivered with pneumatic tires and soda-acid chemical tanks supplying a single hose reel.

Over the years that followed, the soda-acid tanks on the American La France equipment were replaced with plain water tanks plumbed into the rotary pumps.

With only one exception, all fire apparatus delivered to the Los Angeles County Fire Department at that time came equipped with pneumatic tires. The exception was an American La France Type 75 assigned to the Olive View Sanitarium facilities in 1926.

Later on, time and experience would prove that the American La France equipment had "what it took" to last longer and perform better than the REO or Stutz apparatus. Forced by the scarcity of new

This photo shows the contents of one of the 12 fire trailers placed throughout Los Angeles County during 1920. (See pg. 2)

*Arnold Muench photo, Forestry Dept. Archives*

Fire District trailer #4, assigned in 1921 to the Topanga District, is shown here being towed by the third vehicle ever assigned to the F & FW, a used 1917 Ford Model "T" phaeton. Twelve such trailers were placed wherever funds were raised for $600 cost of building and equipping each trailer. (See pg. 2)

*James Turner collection*

Dissolved in 1928, shortly after being formed, the Las Flores Canyon District sported this 1928 Chevrolet. Mechanical specs on this short-lived unit are not available, and its ultimate fate is unknown. The Ford Model "T" at left is undoubtedly a volunteer rig.

*Unknown photographer*

apparatus and parts for the old apparatus during the World War II years, the old "Frogs," as they were called, lasted well into the years of 1948, 1949, and even into 1950. Some of this apparatus was in reserve status, but some of it also was first line equipment.

Neither the REO-Obenchain-Boyer nor the Stutz apparatus had the lasting power of the Frogs. Most of them were placed in reserve or sold prior to World War II. No doubt, few could foretell the rapidly increasing amount of heavy service these smaller pumpers would experience during the 1930's era.

Due to Los Angeles County's characteristic of being a rural or semi-rural jurisdiction during the 1920's, no thought was given to the purchase of ladder trucks. It was not until 1949 that such consideration was given. The Hollywood and Sherman Districts joined the newly formed Consolidated Fire Protection District in 1950, when the first aerial ladder truck was purchased and numbered Truck 8.

As previously stated, by the late 1920's, it had already become apparent that a few of the REO and Stutz pumpers were no match for the demands of their respective districts. Replacement apparatus began to arrive for stations having the smaller apparatus. Moneta-Gardena Station 22 and City Terrace Station 32 received new American La France Type 75 750 G.P.M. pumpers with 80 gallon capacity tank in 1926. When Altadena Station 12 was new, it received a new 1928 750 G.P.M. Seagrave pumper with a 100 gallon capacity tank and an F6 engine. In 1929 Santa Fe Springs received a replacement 1000 G.P.M. Seagrave pumper with a 100 gallon capacity tank. Seagrave 750 G.P.M. pumpers were received in 1930 to replace equipment at Santa Fe Springs Station 17 (E-15), Flintridge Station 28, and Walnut Park Station 24. Singleton American La France 750 pumpers were installed at San Dimas Station 25 in 1926 and at new Station 22 in Belvedere Gardens in 1931.

Belvedere District Volunteer Station 1 was the proud owner of this 1924 Reo La France chemical wagon. Both shifts are present. Note red lenses in head lights.

*Richard Henze photo*
*from the collection of*
*John Whelan*

So new that three men still have makeshift turnout coats, West Hollywood District's 1924 American La France type 75 750 G.P.M. pumper gleams in the morning sun. This model had chain drive.

*Hiram Swallow collection*

On this overcast day in 1937, Station 20 in Norwalk shows off its original equipment 1924 Stutz 500 G.P.M. pumper.

*Dale Magee photo*

Belvedere Gardens Engine 3, original equipment 1924 American La France with 750 G.P.M. rotary pump. Note that the 24' ladder has been moved to the left side.

*From the collection of Dale Magee*

Puente District's Engine 26, original equipment 1924 Reo-Obenchain-Boyer. This photo was taken one year too soon to show the windshield, which was added in 1938.

*Dale Magee photo*

Showing considerable wear and tear in this 1937 photo is Volunteer Engine 33, Palmdale. Most of these 1923 Reo La France rigs did not hold up well for very long.

*Dale Magee collection*

This 1937 photo shows Rescue Co. #1 out of Altadena Station 11 to still be in excellent condition. A used 1922 Lincoln, with body by the fire shops, it was originally donated by a citizen named Archie Andrews

*Dale Magee collection*

Shown here in 1937 backing into quarters, Engine 12's 1928 Seagrave 750 G.P.M. pumper is still entirely original.

*Dale Magee photo*

Still brand new, Engine 12's 1928 Seagrave shows the original light configuration—before the windshield added in 1938 and sealed beam headlights added in 1948. Engines 18 & 24 received identical rigs.

*Dale Magee collection*

Engine 18 (Lennox) shows several modifications to its 1928 Seagrave 750 G.P.M. pumper in this 1951 photo, among them sealed beam headlights, electro-mechanical siren, windshield and updated red lights on top of the windshield. This rig would serve one more year.

*Dale Magee collection*

Flintridge engine 28 shows off its second apparatus, a 1930 Seagrave 750 G.P.M. pumper with 100 gallon tank. This rig replaced the original 1924 Reo, which was sold to Lancaster. Engine 15 received an identical rig. They were the first Seagraves delivered with dual rear wheels and 4-wheel brakes.

*Dale Magee collection*

Santa Fe Springs Engine 17's 1,000 G.P.M. 1930 Seagrave pumper in front of the station in 1951. Note radio speaker on top of gasoline tank; a very early installation.

*Dale Magee collection*

Taken when brand new in 1931, this photo shows Santa Fe Springs 2nd Engine. This 750 G.P.M. pumper served with Engine 17's 1,000 G.P.M. Seagrave in the same house.

*L.A. Co. Fire photo*

The only one of its kind purchased by L.A. County, Belvedere Gardens Engine 22, a 1931 American La France Model 279 750 G.P.M. pumper remained in service until 1950. This was the last district rig purchased until the Depression waned in 1938.

*L.A. Co. Fire photo from the collection of Dale Magee*

A rare factory photo of the 1924 American La France 750 pumper, which was the first Engine 12, Signal Hill Fire Protection District. After Signal Hill incorporated in 1925, the number 12 was reissued in 1928 to West Altadena.

*American La France photo from the collection of Dale Magee*

The only known delivery photo of solid-tired Engine 46's Type 38 1926 750 G.P.M. American La France. This rig never left the hospital grounds at Olive View Sanitarium, Sylmar.

*American La France photo from the collection of Dale Magee*

Captain McIntyre stands next to San Dimas Engine 25, a 1926 American La France 350 G.P.M. pumper. Call men filled out the rest of the crew.

*Carson photo*

# III Second-Generation Forestry Apparatus 1937-1953

With the demise of the Moreland Truck Corporation toward the end of the Great Depression, a new source of supply for Forester and Fire Warden fire apparatus became necessary. The first such units were delivered by Seagrave. These 1938 "Waterfall" Model rigs were 500 G.P.M. pumper/tankers. The tanks were of 600 gallon capacity. Engines were the smaller Seagrave V-12.

Designated as Pumpers "S" through "W", they were assigned to fill Division Headquarters Stations

Factory photos of the last two-tone green V-12 Seagrave delivered to the F & FW. Note the enclosed overhead 20' extension ladder and nested 14' roof ladder. This 1940 model featured the standard 500 G.P.M. pump, 600 gallon water tank and L.A. County-specified louvered hood vents, and was assigned to Soledad Headquarters.

*Seagrave Factory photos*

at Arroyo Seco in La Cañada, Soledad in Newhall, Malibu, and San Dimas. As was the custom, the pumpers already in service at those stations were "bumped down" to outlying stations.

For example, Pumper "G" at Arroyo Seco was bumped down to Eaton Canyon Patrol Station. Eaton Canyon's Pumper "Q" was bumped down to become a second engine at San Dimas Headquarters, and later to Bell Gardens E-39.

All of the new Seagrave units had some of the same basic specifications as the Morelands preceding them. However, they were more powerful, faster, and easier to operate, being equipped with the smaller Seagrave V-12 200 horsepower engines, lower-geared steering, and vacuum booster brakes.

The year 1940 brought about delivery of one more of this type of Seagrave. It was assigned to Fire Station 40 in the Pico District. Painted Killarney

One of three identical 1950 Mack Model "L" triple combinations delivered to Malibu Station 69 in Topanga Canyon. The other two went to present Station 66 as Engine 85 and to Station 46.

*L.A. Co. Fire photo*

Pumper "S" (N 346) a two-tone green 1938 model 66E Seagrave V-12 with a 500 G.P.M. pump and 600 gallon tank, a hand-me-down from present Station 82 in 1941. A new louvered hood had replaced the standard Seagrave hood in order to aid with engine overheating problems. Cotton-jacketed 1" hose had become standard on the reels in 1938.

*Dale Magee photo*

This photo shows a handsome 1941 Mack Model "L" pumper/tanker with enclosed ladders on top alongside the suction hoses. This was the last one of four new full-sized apparatus delivered to the F & FW just prior to World War II. This one became E-82 after the war (N556).

*Dale Magee photo*

Green, it was the last Seagrave purchased for the Forester and Fire Warden until 1963.

Just prior to the outbreak of World War II, the Forester and Fire Warden had its last opportunity for several years to purchase new apparatus. This was also the case with the Fire Protection Districts.

The years 1940 and 1941 saw the purchase of four Macks. One was a Type 80, 500 G.P.M. pumper/tanker. The other three were Model L 500 G.P.M. pumpers with 600 gallon capacity tanks. One of the four was assigned to Soledad Headquarters Station, one to Arroyo Seco Headquarters, and the other two to the Malibu Division. These were the last engines delivered from the factory with the two-toned green paint scheme.

The green trucks remained green until they were repainted olive drab, ostensibly for wartime camouflage purposes. After the war, they were painted red as the Forester and Fire Warden began preparations to combine with the Fire Protection Districts.

Immediately after World War II, the need for replacing the older Forester and Fire Warden equipment became acute. The original 1929–36 Moreland pumper/tanker apparatus were still in first line service, as was the small White tanker at Fire Station 39,

the Moreland squads and Pumper "P", the 1933 Mack.

The last true Forester and Fire Warden station had been constructed in 1937. This was the Monte Nido Station in the Malibu Division, currently Fire Station 67. No further expansion was contemplated. Movement toward combining the Forester and Fire Warden with the Fire Protection Districts was already well underway, even at the time the new Forester and Fire Warden apparatus was purchased from 1948 through 1950. No more green fire engines! All this later equipment came from the factory painted Los Angeles County Fire Department red.

Mack was chosen to supply the Forester and Fire Warden with several Model "L" 500 G.P.M. pumpers with 600 gallon capacity tanks. These units were powered with the famous Mack Thermodyne engines with Stromberg dual carburetors "to be adjusted only by a factory representative," according to the guarantee.

Had it not been for the entry of the Crown Coach Company of Los Angeles into the fire engine field in 1953, it seems likely that many more of these rugged, powerful, and smooth-running engines would have been purchased by the County of Los Angeles.

The F & FW's last Fish & Game & Fire patrol boat—the "Grey Gull" idles in the waters of the Catalina Channel watching for poachers, smugglers, rum runners, or whatever. An all wood craft, it had a normal crew of two, a Hall Scott gasoline engine and a 38 G.P.M. Pacific portable pump supplying a 1" hose line for fire fighting.

*L.A. Co. Forestry photo*

This 1937 photo found the "Cobra," the Deptartment's second patrol boat, approaching the dock in L.A. Harbor. It was replaced in 1938 by the Grey Gull, which was similarly equipped. No photo of the Department's first craft, the "Ethel" could be located for this book.

*L.A. Co. Forestry Photo*

The F & FW's command trailer at the Pacoima Warehouse in 1942. This three-sectioned unit was used until the combining of the F & FW and the districts in the mid 1950's.

*L.A. Co. Forestry photo*

The business end of the 1937 Chevrolet panel truck remote communications truck. This 50-watt unit could talk to the command trailer and L.A. H.Q. on N. Spring St. in Los Angeles if the distance were not too great and no hills were in the way.

*L.A. Co. Forestry photo*

(*Above and Left*) Several slip-on 500 G.P.M. pumper/tanker units were given to the L.A. County Fire Dept. during WW II for volunteer civilian use. This 1938 GMC truck, stationed at Arroyo Seco H.Q. in La Cañada, was one of them. All working features except the pump were homemade.

*L.A. Co. Forestry photo*

Four photos showing Malibu Division Patrol 65's 1942 International half-ton pickup patrol, its hose reel and radio installations. This 50 G.P.M. PTO pump could take suction from an outside source as well as from its 75 gallon tank.

*Hiram Swallow Collection*

Among the first F&FW engines to be delivered from the factory painted red was this 1949 "C" Model Mack 500 G.P.M. pumper with 600 gallon tank. It went to Pine Canyon Station 78.

*L.A. Co. Fire photo*

Fire Warden Bill Wing with the Department's new 1946 Allis-Chalmers HD-10 tractor with bull-dozer. This was the Department's 5th tractor.

*L.A. Co. fire photo*

F W 3, a well-used Caterpillar Model D-7 off loading from its low-boy, Topanga Canyon, 1948.

*L.A. Co. fire photo*

A 1939 White cabover crew truck arrives for training at Hastings Ranch. Rig at left is probably Pumper G.

*L.A. Co. Forestry photo*

Engineer Vernon May stands ready to repaint Engine 82's Model "L" 1941 Mack with L.A. Co. red. 1948 was the last year of the green Forestry rigs.

*L.A. Co. Forestry photo*

Privately owned by a wealthy Flintridge resident, this former City of Pasadena 1916 Seagrave pumper supplemented the Flintridge Fire Protection District's fire protection during World War II. It is currently in a museum in Lake Tahoe, Nevada.

*From the collection of Dale Magee*

Built on a modified 1936 Ford truck chassis, this lighting plant was used to illuminate the main fire camp during an extended period fire. It was designed by Forester L. S. Percey, and fabricated in the Mission St. shops.

*Arnold Muench photo, L.A. Co. Forestry Dept*

This 1927 Pierce Arrow Bus was used for the transportation of Juvenile Camp Crew personnel to work projects. Forester Reinmuller stands in front of this 33-passenger beauty.

*Arnold Muench photo*

Taken about 1948, this photo shows N 567, a 1940 Seagrave model 66E with a 500 G.P.M. pump and 600 gallon tank, reloading hose on Georgian Rd., next to present Fire Station 82. It has yet to be painted red.

*L. Arnold collection*

This handsome 1940 Mack Model "E" 500 G.P.M. pumper with 600 gallon tank was first delivered to Soledad Division H.Q. in Newhall. The contrast between the forest green fenders and Kilarney green body is evident here.

*Dale Magee collection*

San Dimas H.Q. Engine 86 (presently Engine 64) parked in front of the station. The common 500 G.P.M. pump and 600 gallon tank are featured on this 1941 model, and it has been repainted red (N 556).

*L. Arnold collection*

N 362, a 1938 Ford Utility truck assigned to the F & FW and operating in the unincorporated area south of Station 9. This green truck shows the original County Forestry badge painted on the door.

*L. Arnold collection*

Utilizing W.W.II flame thrower technology, Forester Vernon May demonstrates the "new" 1947 trailer-mounted back-firing torch. This unit remained in service until the late '60s.

*L.A. County Forestry photo*

A slightly fuzzy photo of a 1934 Chevrolet Patrol in front of the Paramount Patrol Station, Malibu.

*Des Barton collection*

# IV Second-Generation Fire District Apparatus 1932-1953

1938 through 1948 were years of rapid change with respect to the size and capabilities of pumpers purchased by the Los Angeles County Fire Protection Districts.

The original REO-Obenchain-Boyer and Stutz rigs were rapidly outclassed by the number and size of fires they were expected to handle. A few had been replaced by 1938; the rest were replaced or relocated in the years immediately following. They were just not up to the task at hand.

All of the original American La France Type 75 rotary pumpers remained in service well into the post–World War II years, often serving as reserve apparatus.

From 1937 to 1938, the Seagrave Company of Columbus, Ohio, supplied new, faster, and more powerful triple combination pumpers. Each pumper was equipped with a 904 V-12 Seagrave engine, a 1,000 G.P.M. main pump, a single hose reel plumbed to a 120 gallon capacity water tank, and a hose bed that carried 1,000 feet of 2-1/2 inch hose with space below in front of the tailboard for 1-1/2 inch hose packs. These pumpers went to Stations 1 and 3 in the Belvedere District, Station 8 in Hollywood, Station 10 in Downey, Station 14 in Howard, Station 19 in La Crescenta, Station 20 in Norwalk, and Station 38 in Angeles Mesa.

A notable exception to these "standard" specifi-

A Seagrave factory photo of Truck 23, Bellflower, the Department's third ladder truck. This 1953 85' Aerial last served the Department as the first Truck 82, La Cañada, placed in service as a one-man truck in 1972.

*Dale Magee Collection*

cations was the 1938 Seagrave placed in service at Norwalk Fire Protection District Station 20. The Norwalk District was quite large, the terrain was flat, and, except for a few residential and farm ranch buildings, consisted largely of grassland and row crops. Fire hydrants were few and far between. Designed by Chief Mechanical Inspector Wallace E. Powellson, Station 20's Seagrave featured a 2,500 gallon capacity water tank, which compensated for the lack of fire hydrants in that District. It was the largest piece of tanker fire apparatus west of Chicago at the time of its delivery. Fully loaded, it weighed 52,000 lbs.

Other equipment included vacuum booster brakes, a set of "fog" applicators carried on the sides of the tank, a 55 ft. extension ladder located above the tank, four 1-1/2 inch preconnected hose lines, and two 1-inch preconnected hose lines discharging from the rear. It also carried 1,000 feet of 2-1/2 inch hose.

A five-man crew was assigned to operate this behemoth. According to those who operated the big rig, it took a great deal of practice to develop the skills necessary to turn a corner and to bring the apparatus to a safe stop reasonably close to the desired location. The lurching action, instigated by the movement of the large water load, gear shifting, turning and

stopping, earned Engine 20 the nickname of the "Galloping Ghost."

With the advent of World War II, new fire apparatus almost ceased being delivered to fire departments throughout the United States. The Los Angeles County Fire Department was placed in ninth position on a priority rating scale of 1 to 10. Military requirements first needed to be met. By 1942 the Department had worked its way up into third position priority.

This allowed the Department to purchase two Ford La France pumpers, a Dodge General, and two Mack Model "E" rigs. All five were 500 G.P.M. pumpers with 200 gallon capacity water tanks. One of the Macks was assigned to new Fire Station 52 in East Altadena, and the other to Station 29 in Baldwin Park Valley Fire Protection District. All of these rigs were notoriously underpowered.

With the exception of the Macks, the other apparatus went into reserve or relief status within five years after World War II. One of the Ford La France rigs became a crash truck at Fire Station 111 at Brackett Airfield near Pomona after serving Station 83.

Other wartime apparatus received from the federal government, under the auspices of the office of Civil Defense, were 12 Coventry trailer pumpers. Powered by Chrysler 6-cylinder engines, which drove

Walnut Park Engine 24's crew tries on the new MSA demand-type breathing apparatus next to their new 1951 International Model R-203 1,000 gallon pumper.

*L.A. Co. Fire photo*

Taken in 1952, this photo shows Engine 11's 1948 Seagrave "Waterfall" J-1000 1,000 G.P.M. pumper with 500 gallon tank in front of the original station at 910 E. Foothill Blvd. (Altadena Dr.). Note one reel of cotton jacketed hose and one reel of rubber.

*Dale Magee photo*

Engine 16's 1948 Seagrave Model J-1000 pumper is just nicely broken in in this 1951 photograph. Note both reel lines are still hard rubber. Personnel over 6' in height could actually reach the nozzle to pull the line.

*Dale Magee collection*

(*Left and above*) Laguna Engine 2's Art Deco 1941 American La France 1,500 gallon tanker/pumper. This unit finished its days in reserve as Engine 273, Newhall, in 1954.

*Dale Magee Collection*

500 G.P.M. centrifugal pumps, this equipment was placed in strategically located areas throughout the county. They were to be used in the event of air raids or other wartime demands.

At the end of World War II, a scramble began. Every civilian fire agency in the United States placed orders for new fire apparatus of all types. In Los Angeles County, many pumpers still in service through the mid-40's dated back to 1924 and were original fire district equipment!

In 1948, ten very welcome Seagrave Model J-1000's, 1,000 G.P.M. triple combinations were delivered. Built to new District specifications, included were 500 gallon capacity water tanks, 268 horsepower Seagrave V-12 engines, divided hose beds for laying two 2-1/2 inch hose lines when necessary, two 1-1/2 inch preconnected hose lines, two hose reels for 1-inch cotton or rubber hose, vacuum booster brakes, adjustable driver seats, and 3-way FM radios.

This series of Seagrave equipment proved to be unsatisfactory with respect to hill-climbing ability, but they were adequate in flatland districts. In all cases, engines tended to overheat on hot summer days, on long runs, and on long pumping assignments. Pumping with one or both hoods open was a common practice.

During the late 1940's, as the organizational groundwork within the Department began to be established in preparation for the combining of the Forester and Fire Warden and the Fire Protection Districts, the development of a new style of pumper was necessitated. Requirements called for a piece of fire apparatus suited to the long, high-speed responses demanded on brush fire alarms in addition to the day-to-day short intra-district runs. Built around a Kenworth chassis and a 275 horsepower Hall Scott six-cylinder gasoline engine, this next series of apparatus was designed to handle any sort of incident.

Then-Bn 2 Chief Keith Klinger poses in front of original Station 17 in Santa Fe Springs by his 1947 Ford Chief's car, circa 1948.

*L.A. Co. Fire photo*

A 1953 photo of Chief Engineer Cecil R. Gehr at Fire Station 4 in South San Gabriel. Since the late 1920's Oldsmobiles and Buicks were the car of choice for the Chief Engineer. Fords are the current choice.

*L.A. Co. Fire photo*

The first of these engines was delivered during the summer of 1950. The order consisted of nine such units assembled by the General Pacific Corporation in its Los Angeles facility. Coachwork to the rear of the cab was supplied by the Coast Company of Martinez, California. These pumpers had 1,000 G.P.M. Hale main pumps, 500 gallon capacity water tanks, and 90 G.P.M. Oberdorfer road pumps. They were assigned to Stations 6, 7, 12, 22, 54, and 70.

Two additional units came with 750 G.P.M. main pumps, a smaller Waukeshau engine, and a correspondingly smaller hood and grill. These units were assigned to Station 60 at Universal Studios and to Station 33 in Lancaster as Engine 233.

During the years 1950 through 1952, eighteen additional pumpers similar to the General Pacific

equipment were delivered. These were International Harvester Model R-203 pumpers, which utilized the same engine, tank, and pump specifications as the General Pacifics.

The first few of the Internationals were delivered without doors for the cab. Later deliveries with doors made little difference to some stations. They merely removed the doors in order to provide better intra-cab ventilation during hot weather, especially during brush fire season. The Internationals were the last pieces of apparatus delivered to Los Angeles County without power steering.

Due to the heritage of the International Harvester name, these engines were almost always referred to as the "Cornbinders."

Consolidated F.P.D. Engine 182 (currently 82) shortly after delivery to its La Cañada station. Capt. Lyman Whitlatch, unknown Engineer, Fireman Ray Harrel, and Fireman Paul Van de Wettering next to their 1952 Model R-203 International Harvester 1,000 G.P.M. pumper with 500 gallon tank. Note new style double doughnut rolls of 1" cotton hose on top of 1-1/2" hose bed.

*Dale Magee collection*

Engineer Ray Stohl poses proudly next to newly delivered 1952 International Harvester assigned to Altadena Station 52. As did all "Cornbinders," this unit came with a 1,000 G.P.M. main pump, 90 G.P.M. Oberdorfer road pump, and a 500 gallon tank.

*Dale Magee photo*

Central Manufacturing District (Commerce) Truck 27, the Department's second ladder truck shortly after delivery. This 1951 American La France with 85' aerial ladder served until 1971 when it was replaced by a rear-mount American La France 100' Aerial.

*L.A. Co. Fire photo*

This 1942 Dodge-General 500 G.P.M. pumper with a 200 gallon tank replaced the 1938 Ford taken over from the Rosemead Volunteer Fire Department when it joined the L.A. County Valley Fire Protection District in 1942.

*Dale Magee collection*

Lakewood's Engine 45, a 1948 "High-Reeler" Seagrave with a 1,000 G.P.M. pumper and a 500 gallon tank during its acceptance pump test at the Zonal St. Shops, Aug. 3, 1948.

*Glen Alton photo*

Engine 54's 1949 General-Pacific 1,000 G.P.M. pumper pumps a full 4-way valve hookup during a drill at an unknown location.

*Dale Magee collection*

This 1947 Ford half-ton panel was typical of the early rescue units found throughout the L.A. County Fire Dept. at the time of this 1951 photo. Both Fords and Chevrolets were used until 1961 when a few Dodges were purchased.

*Dale Magee collection*

(*Right and Above*) Two views of Station 17's 1948 Ford 1/2-ton panel truck rescue unit shortly after delivery. Such units were the norm until the arrival of the Paramedics in the early 70's.

*L.A. Co. Fire Dept. photos*

Originally delivered to the Forestry Department as Pumper "Q" in 1934, this White 250 G.P.M. pumper with a 200 gallon tank here becomes Bell Gardens' first "real" fire engine. Note that the 1" hose reel on top has been removed and the plumbing redirected.

*Dale Magee collection*

This March 22, 1958 photo of Lakewood Engine 245's 1950 "Cornbinder" in action is undoubtedly one of the best ever taken. It is shown here pumping two very long 2-1/2" hose lines at the enormous Hancock oil refinery fire in March, 1958.

*L.A. Co. Fire Dept. photo*

A factory photo of Pico Engine 40's 1940 Seagrave 500 G.P.M. pumper. Built to Forestry specifications, including the 600 gallon tank and no 2-1/2" hose, it was later painted red. Later plumbing and compartment changes allowed it to carry some 2-1/2" hose.

*Dale Magee collection*

A factory photo of Hollywood District's Engine 8. This V-12 1938 Sweetheart model 1,000 G.P.M. pumper with 80 gallon tank replaced the original 1924 American La France, which went into reserve (relief).

*Dale Magee collection*

This 1951 photo, taken at the Elmira, N.Y. factory, shows Central Manufacturing District Truck 27 just prior to shipment to L.A. Co. Truck 8 (1950) and Truck 3 (1954) were identical 85' Aerials.

*American La France Photo*

A 1951 L Model Mack 750 G.P.M. pumper purchased that year and sent to Station 35 in Cerritos. Until the arrival of the Crown apparatus in 1954–55, this make was preferred over all others for both district and F & FW work during the 40's and 50's.

*Dale Magee collection*

La Crescenta District's Engine 19, a 1938 Seagrave "Sweetheart" model shortly after delivery. This 750 G.P.M. pumper with 100 gallon tank served until 1955. Note mud tires on all wheels, and the Forker Helmets on each side rail for use of the call men at the scene.

*Dale Magee photo*

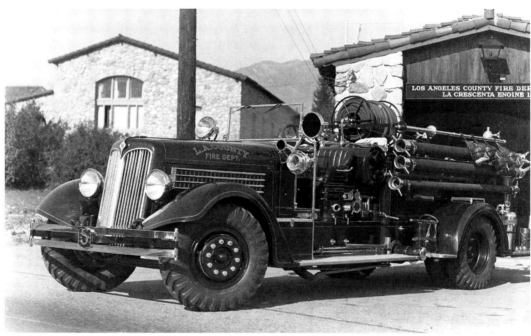

Clearwater-Hynes Station 31's 1941 American La France 1,000 G.P.M. pumper (1,500 gallon tank) basks in the sun awaiting a response. Identical apparatus was installed in Laguna Station 2 and Florence Station 9.

*L. Arnold photo*

Two views of the "Galloping Ghost," the 1938 Sweetheart model Seagrave pumper/tanker with 900 G.P.M. (rated) main pump and 2,500 gallon tank. Note generator for two large demountable floodlights; also, four large fog applicators for indirect attack. The 55' aluminum extension ladder is in place. It carried 1,250' of 2-1/2" hose, 1,350' of 1-1/2" hose, and weighed 52,000 lbs. fully loaded.

*Dale Magee collection*

These two 1944 "E" Model Mack 750 G.P.M. pumpers with 200 gallon tanks were assigned to Altadena Station 52 (FD30) and Baldwin Park Station 29 (FD 31). Wartime deliveries such as these were rare.

*L. Arnold photos*

E-34                A rare photo assemblage showing all four 1942 Model "L" Mack (1,000 gallon pump and 1,000 gallon tank). Note that Engine 4 has no hose reels.

*L. Arnold photos*

E-4

E-14

E-5

A beautiful night photo of former Engine 22's 1949 General-Pacific, here in action as Reserve 514 out of Station 13 (Commerce).

*L. Arnold photo*

The unincorporated "5 Points" area east of El Monte was served for many years by this 1939 "EE" Model Mack (500 G.P.M. pump, 400 gallon tank). An identical rig served Station 41, and later, Station 94.

*Dot and Larry photo*

L. to R., Patrol 56's 1957 Chevrolet Patrol, Engine 56's 1948 Seagrave, and Engine 83's 1942 Ford/La France participate in a 1-1/2" brush fire hose lay drill with 1" tap-ins somewhere on the Palos Verdes Peninsula about 1960.

*Gustavson collection*

Engine 12's 1949 General-Pacific 1,000 G.P.M. pumper with 500 gallon tank on the day of its delivery in July of 1950. 1" reel line hose has not yet been changed over to cotton-jacketed brush hose.

*Dale Magee photo*

One of the Coventry pumpers given to the Department during World War II is shown being given a workout by Civil Defense Volunteers, under Captain Keith Klinger of Station 5, in 1943.

*Dot & Larry photo*

Taken in April of 1951 in front of Santa Fe Springs Station 17, the Battalion 2 Ladies' Auxiliary commissary unit poses for the camera. This converted bakery truck was built on a 1936 Chevrolet chassis and was used during large fires in the San Gabriel Valley.

*L.A. Co. Fire photo*

Its district annexed by Compton, Engine 51's 1924 American La France is completely stripped and ready to head for the shops and reserve status in 1948.

*L.A. Co. Fire photo*

One of the seven Weed Abatement Section's 1946 Willys/Ford "Jeeps" displays its 25 G.P.M. pump over a 70 gallon tank. These were used to control errant weed-burning fires undertaken by the Department in the suburban areas. A few were used as Patrol units in the outlying F & FW areas.

*L.A. Co. Fire photo*

Chatsworth Patrol 75's 1946 Dodge Power Wagon Patrol with 100 gallon tank and 75 G.P.M. pump is shown next to the station in 1950. It is surprising that many more of these 4-wheel drive vehicles were not purchased for this purpose.

*L.A. Co. Fire photo*

This 1942 Ford La France 500 G.P.M. pumper and its sister rig were bumped down from Stations 13, 21, 30, 83, and 111 (Brackett Field, Pomona) until placed into reserve in the middle 1950's.

*Walt Pittman photo*

# V Third-Generation Apparatus (District & F&FW Combined) 1954-1972

Probably no other make of fire apparatus has had the ultimate overall impact on the Los Angeles County Fire Department as has the Crown "Firecoach." Until the early 1950's, this Los Angeles-based company had specialized in the manufacture of school buses. Occasionally, as early as 1936, Crown Coach had done some custom fire apparatus work. But it was not until 1953 that Crown Coach offered a complete line of fire apparatus. Features such as power steering, the new cab-forward design, a short turning radius, and the powerful Hall Scott gasoline engine made them unique.

All deliveries to the Los Angeles County Fire Department specified an additional feature—that of standardized compartmentalization for interior storage of auxiliary equipment such as air masks, nozzles, suction and bypass hoses, first aid equipment, and salvage covers.

Taken in 1958, Engine 208's 1938 Seagrave 1,000 gallon pumper poses for the photographer. Note hose reel has been moved to the rear to accommodate the demountable monitor.

*George Bass photo*

By 1953, practically all apparatus that had not recently been replaced by the General Pacifics and the International Harvesters were at the end of their service lives. In addition, new fire stations were being constructed at a rapid pace. An order to meet the demand was placed with Crown Coach Company for 40 triple combination pumpers to be delivered over a two-year period.

The first Crown Coach fire engine was delivered to Station 40 in the Pico area on June 1, 1954. It had a 1,250 G.P.M. main pump and a 500 gallon capacity water tank. It also had two 1-inch hose reels, as did all the "Flatlander" apparatus. Several Crowns such as those delivered to Station 8 in West Hollywood were equipped with 1,500 G.P.M. pumps. A number of the Crowns that were deliv-

Engine 14's brand new Crown 1,250 triple combination pumper w/ 500 gallon tank, taken April 29, 1955.

*B.N. Landrum photo, Hiram Swallow collection*

Three of these Crown 1,250 pumpers were delivered in 1957 through L.A. Co. Fire to Kuwait for use in their extensive new oil refining facilities. They featured the 1091 Hall Scott engine and a 400 gallon tank.

*Warren Bowen photo*

An acceptance pump test for one of the new 1955 Crown 1,250 G.P.M. pumpers at the Training Center drafting pit.

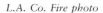

*L.A. Co. Fire photo*

South San Dimas' Engine 141's 1972 Ward La France poses near the station. In beautiful condition, this rig is still in service at the time of this writing.

*L.A. Co. Fire photo*

ered to the Forester and Fire Warden "brush stations" came equipped with 600 gallon capacity water tanks.

As of this writing, many of the Crown Coach fire engines, especially the 1974 through 1977 models are still in first-line service. These engines have either relatively low mileage on their odometers, have been repowered, or have undergone at least a major overhaul of the power train.

In later years, a few Crown Coach "snorkel" ladder trucks were ordered. Most of these are currently in reserve status. In addition, a few "squirt" telescoping boom units were ordered along with several miscellaneous pieces of equipment.

Station 11's 1961 Crown pumper with 935 Hall Scott Engine, 1,250 main pump and 500 gallon tank poses next to its companion 1961 Dodge Rescue, the last non-paramedic style squad for this Altadena station. E-11's 10-speed split rear and transmission was put to good use in the steep hills.

*L.A. Co. Fire photo*

A pre-delivery photo of Engine 50's 1955 Crown 1,250 pumper.

*Warren Bowen photo*

Watts Engine 209's Crown (FD 222) showing the optional convertible top available for such apparatus.

*Warren Bowen photo*

Cudahy Engine 147, a 1953 International/Coast 1,000 G.P.M. pumper (#49277) with a 935 Hall Scott engine poses at its short-lived station in Cudahy in 1971. This was former Huntington Park Engine 3, and served as E-147 for one year, when the station was closed.

*L. Arnold photo*

1954 saw this large order of Crown pumpers delivered to L.A. County from the factory in Los Angeles. All but four had 1,250 G.P.M. pumps and 500 gallon tanks and were powered with the Hall Scott engine rated at 295 H.P. Stations 8, 9, 17, and 27 received 1,500 G.P.M. pumps with 320 H.P. Hall Scotts.

*Crown Coach Photo, L. Arnold collection*

Glendora Engine 152's 1961 Crown 1,000 G.P.M. pumper (F-1270) shows its open cab next to newly delivered closed-cabbed Engine 144's 1968 Crown 1,000 G.P.M. pumper at the training center.

*L.A. Co. Fire photo*

Commerce Engine 27's "Hog," a 1965 Crown 1,500 G.P.M. pumper with 400 gallon tank. This rig featured a pre-plumbed monitor and transverse hose beds for both 1-1/2" and 2-1/2" hose as well as a front suction.

*L. Arnold collection*

Engine 35's 1970 American La France "Pioneer" model 1,000 G.P.M. pumper with 400 gallon tank, one of four such apparatus delivered to Fire Stations 15, 122, 35, and 110 (P-1-2055).

*C. Madderom photo*

Engine 48's refurbished 1968 Crown Diesel with 1,250 G.P.M. pumper and 500 gallon tank on display. This series was the last to use the inadequate electronic siren. 1972 introduced the Federal Model "Q" for all large apparatus (F-1548).

*C. Madderom photo*

Engine 58's new Crown Pumper was able to be restored to full service after being burned in the "Liberty" Fire in Malibu in 1958.

*Warren Bowen Photo at the Crown factory*

Two factory photos of the first Crown delivered to L.A. County Fire Department in June of 1954. This unit featured the 935 Hall Scott engine and a 500 gallon tank (F-1017.).

*Crown factory photos*

Belvedere Engine Co. 1's 1954 Crown 1,250 G.P.M. pumper performing at a frame garage fire with spread into an adjoining neighborhood market, Nov. 25, 1960.

*L..A. Co. Fire photo*

Engine 1's Crown and crew fight off intense radiated heat as this garage fire spreads into an adjacent market.

*L.A. Co. Fire photo*

A move-up company near the Sierra Madre brush area, Engine 108's 1972 Ward La France, complete with roadrunner under the jump seat window, on a move-up to Station 5.

*L.A. Co. Fire photo, courtesy L. Arnold*

This sedan cabbed 1963 Crown was one of 3 purchased for brush engines 82, 73, and 80. All featured the 1091 Hall-Scott engine, a 1,250 G.P.M. pump and a 500 gallon tank. (Co. #49563.)

*George Bass photo*

This 1957 International training rig at the Cecil R. Gehr Training Center was later pressed into service as Engine 401 and then retired from service by 1980.

*George Bass photo*

Shown here at Universal Studios, 1965 Crown open cab is still with open cab today, and owned by the Museum Association (49215).

*L. Arnold photo*

One of two sedan-cabbed 1963 Seagrave pumpers with 1,000 G.P.M. pumps and 500 gallon tanks purchased for brush area stations. These were among the last having 10-speed split rear end transmissions and Hall-Scott gasoline engines prior to switching to diesel automatics.

*George Bass photo*

This 1959 Crown "Toyopet" pumper with 1,000 G.P.M. pump and 600 gallon tank was delivered to Fire Station 75 in Chatsworth and another to Malibu Station 70. The 10-speed split rear end transmission remained, but the rubber 1" hose on the reels was replaced with cotton-jacketed brush hose. A total of 10 of these small and under-powered rigs were delivered.

*Dale Magee collection.*

One of two such rigs, Engine 382's 1957 FWD/Yankee/Calavar brush fire apparatus featuring a 750 G.P.M. main pump, 500 gallon tank and carrying only 1" and 1-1/2" hose, shown here in the Pacoima Warehouse yard.

*Larry Arnold collection*

1961 saw the delivery of nine of these Ford/Sabco "400 Series" Type II brush fire apparatus. Designed for fire motorway use, they carried 1" and 1-1/2" hose, a 300 G.P.M. main pump and a 400 gallon tank.

*W. Hattersly photo*

A one-of-a-kind 1,250 G.P.M. pumper with 600 gallon tank by Coast Manufacturing, shown here at its second assignment as Engine 72 in the Malibu Hills. The rack for 12 coils of 1" brush hose has been added behind the reels. This 1958 unit was tolerated until 1972.

*Larry Arnold Collection*

This 1956 open-cabbed Crown (F-1047) with 1,250 main pump and 500 gallon tank was still serviceable enough to be used as Engine 157 in Green Valley, an all call man station in upper San Francisquito Canyon.

*Larry Arnold Collection*

Two for the F & FW. Engines 67, Monte Nido, and 78 in the Leona Valley each received one of these 1958 FWD 750 G.P.M. pumpers with 500 gallon tanks. These FWD factory photos attest to their rugged beauty. These were the last of four FWD units purchased.

*FWD Factory photo; Dale Magee collection*

Two photos of an experimental Ford/Pittman "Fire Arm," forerunner to the "Snorkel" being demonstrated in the Flintridge Hills for interested Bn. 4 personnel, circa 1960.

*E. Wagner photo, Hiram Swallow Collection*

Dominguez Truck 127 85' Crown/Pittman Snorkel poses near its station. These two-axled units were delivered to F.S. 29 in Baldwin Park, 36 in Carson, 43 in Industry, and 127's in Dominguez in 1966 and 1968.

*L.A. Co. Fire photo*

La Mirada's Truck 49 in action at the 1976 William Penn Hotel Fire in Bn. 8, City of Whittier. This dual-axled 85' unit with a 1091 Hall-Scott engine worked for several hours on this major fire.

*L.A. Co. Fire photo*

L.A. Co.'s first Crown/Pittman Snorkel, 75' Truck 43 (Industry) just prior to acceptance tests at the Training Center, August of 1965.

Two views of the 1959 Seagrave 85' Aerial Ladder assigned to Truck 42 in Rosemead, one as delivered with open cab, and one after the fiberglass cab was added in 1972. This truck featured a stick shift and a 1091 Hall Scott engine (N 49619).

Seagrave reserve truck 603 was inherited from the City of Whittier when they joined the Consolidated Fire Protection District. It is actually a Quint, having a hose bed, 1,000 G.P.M. pump, 100 gallon tank and an 85' aerial ladder.

*C. Madderom photo*

A right oblique view of one of the dual-axeled 1968 Crown 85' Crown Pittman aerial platforms, this one replacing the single-axled model at Fire Station 43 (F1544).

*C. Madderom photo*

An example of bumping down to extend useful service life are these two shots of 1966 Crown 75' snorkel in service first as Truck 29 and lastly as Truck 82 (49226) (F-1432).

*L. Arnold photos*

Off-loading the Department's last Caterpillar D-7 tractor with buldozer and hose reel in preparation for the ground-breaking for the present Cecil R. Gehr Training Center in Aug., 1954.

*L.A. Co. Fire photo*

A 1969 photo of a new Caterpillar D-8 tractor with bulldozer on its loading ramp at the Pacoima warehouse. All six tractors used today are this size.

*Jerry Meehan collection*

Transport 5, a 1971 International/Cozad is shown here at Fire Station 125 with its Caterpillar D-8 tractor with bulldozer, ready to respond to the Malibu Hills.

*C. Madderom photo*

The Department's road grader arrives at Catalina Island, along with a 'dozer still on the barge, in order to do fire control motorway clearance, date unknown. This is an annual event.

*Photo courtesy Capt. Rick Harp*

Five of the six Caterpillar D-8's and their tractor/lowboys lines up at the rear of the Pacoima warehouse about 1970. Kenworth, Mack and International trucks are represented here. During the fire season, these units are scattered about the county on local standby.

*L.A. Co. Fire photo*

Never the property of L.A. Co., these two Douglas AJ-1 Savages were leased and on call during the fire season during the 1960's. Both eventually crashed, but during their service time, their 2,000 gallon phoscheck capacity was very welcome on wildland fires.

*L.A. Co. Fire photo*

Two photos showing 'Copter 10 on-loading its 10-man crew at Klinger Center, and the other showing the crew off-loading for fuel break construction south of Mendenhall Peak, upper left center.

*L.A. Co. Fire Dept. photos*

The Department's second helicopter, a Bell 47 G2 at rest at Fire Station 65 in 1972. The 100 gallon aluminum drop tank and stokes rescue litter basket are in place.

*Larry Arnold collection*

The four-place Bell Jet Ranger (Copter 4, later 10) nearest the ground next to the 14-place Copter 14 as both are landing in September of 1973.

*Larry Arnold Collection*

Copter 10, the first large crew carrying and water dropping helicopter put in service in 1967 is shown upon landing at Catalina Island, required pontoons in place. L. to R.: Capt. Phil Finie, Chief Keith Klinger, and Malcomb Renten of the Catalina Island Co.

*Catalina "Islander" photo, courtesy Rick Harp*

Pilot Roland Barton at the controls of the new Bell 47 G2 Helicopter makes an experimental 35 gallon water drop at Klinger Center in 1957. Merely a taste of things to come.

*L.A. Co. Fire photo*

County Fire Department's Bell 47G helicopter shown in 1967 airlifting fire hose into remote area. Pilot can drop all in one spot or scatter hose as he sees fit. Some already has been dropped in this photo.

*L.A. Co. Fire photo*

County Fire Department's Bell 47G helicopter shown in 1967 dumping water into portable sump used with portable pump in remote areas. 'Copter also can make water drop directly onto fire line.

*L.A. Co. Fire photo*

Fireboat 110 moving out from the dock at Marina Del Rey. This 37 ft. unit was built by Campbell in 1974 and features a 1,500 G.P.M. pump and two 212 H.P. Caterpillar diesel engines.

*Jerry Meehan Collection*

A 1958 Crown bus delivered to the L.A. County fire department for recruit/personnel transport to large incidents and special occasions. This was quartered at L.A. H.Q. most of the time.

*Dale Magee collection*

This 1961 Dodge 3/4-ton cab and chassis with custom utility rescue body was one of many purchased by the county. Many of these made the transition from standard rescue service to the first Paramedic units beginning in 1970.

*L. Arnold collection*

A 1973 view of the new L.A. shops near H.Q. Four Crowns and one International/Coast and Truck 20's 1959 Seagrave Aerial are being serviced.

*L. Arnold collection*

The first Light Unit 103 built by the shops on a former International Camp Crew Truck (N4767). This lighting apparatus was transferred to the replacement vehicle in 1974.

*L. Arnold Collection*

Taken in 1979, this photo shows Deluge 87 as built on former Squad 3's Dodge cab & chassis by the shops. This Intelligiant unit had a 2,000 G.P.M. capacity.

*L. Arnold Collection*

One of the last Model R-203 International/Coast 1,000 G.P.M. pumpers to be delivered is this 1952 model for the Flintridge Fire Protection District (now defunct). Personnel are, L. to R., Capt. Harold Jackson, Bn. 4 Chief Roland W. Percey, Chief Deputy Keith E. Klinger, and Chief Engineer Cecil R. Gehr.

*L.A. Co. Fire photo*

A very rare photo showing E-109, the 1960 FWD/Yankee crash truck for Fox Airfield in Lancaster with its tender, the 1939 Seagrave 2,500 gallon tanker/pumper, the Galloping Ghost, originally delivered to Station 20 in Norwalk.

Shown as received from Signal Hill in its white paint scheme, Engine 154's 1963 GMC/Crown 1,250 G.P.M. pumper (F-1322) poses in front of its station.

Central Manufacturing District's Engine 89's 1938 1,000 G.P.M. triple combination pumper awaits the word to return to quarters in this 1952 photo (FD 15).

This yellow 1972 Van Pelt 1,250 G.P.M. pumper was inherited from the City of Claremont when it contracted with L.A. County. It was painted red, saw active service there, and then was placed in reserve in Bn. 4 for several years. It has been sold (Co. #49013).

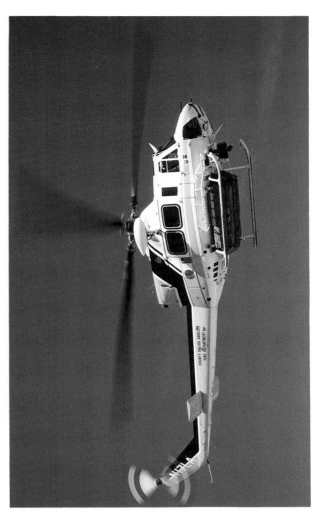

Transport 4's International Transtart tractor (39039) with D-8 Caterpillar tractor with bulldozer parked near F.S. 125 in Malibu.

*Larry Cummings photo*

'Copter 17, a new Bell Model 412, departs the helispot at a recent brush fire near Duarte.

*Kenneth Morris photo*

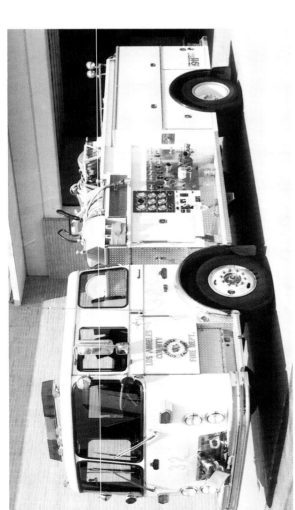

*Larry Arnold photos*

1984 saw the assimilation of the Azusa Fire Department into L.A. County and along with it these two first-line white Crown rigs. The first is a 1981 Crown 1,500 gallon pumper with a 500 gallon tank, front suction, and Stang monitor. It continued on as E-32 and was painted red eventually (F-1864). The second is a rare beast for L.A. County, a 1966 Quint also painted red after being assigned as Truck 24 in Palmdale. It featured a 1,500 G.P.M. pump, 200 gallon tank and a 75' snorkel boom. It is now in reserve (F-1427).

Recently restored by retired Battalion Chief and CEO of JEMS Communications, James O. Page, this 1947 Ford 1/2-ton panel truck was one of the typical post-war units spotted throughout the districts. Internal modifications include a 351 cubic inch "Cleveland" engine, Ford C-6 automatic transmission, power steering and brakes, air conditioning, and electric windows. PPG Delcron paint in L.A. Co. red and correct gold leaf lettering completed the project

*James O. Page collection*

The 1989 GMC field repairman's truck is always a welcome sight during apparatus breakdowns or minor repairs in the field.

*D. Boucher photo*

Captain Ed Rice of Station 73, Newhall, shows off his new 1954 3/4-ton Chevrolet pickup patrol at the Pacoima Warehouse. These trucks, with 75 G.P.M. power take-off pumps and 100 gallon tanks formed the backbone of the brush area fire protection program.

*From the collection of Hiram Swallow*

This 1961 Ford "400" series brush truck was one of nine such units purchased that year for use on back-country dirt roads or motor-ways. It is shown here at Klinger Center prior to equipping for delivery (N 554).

*L.A. Co. Fire photo*

This 1956 International S-180 fuel tender supplied 420 gallons of gasoline or 230 gallons of diesel fuel to apparatus on extended fires. It was later used as a reserve Helitender and placed at Station 74 and the Pacoima Warehouse.

*L.A. Co. Fire photo*

This late 1960's International Flat Bed with diesel fuel supply served the Department into the early seventies while the department transitioned from gasoline to diesel powered apparatus (Co. #40243).

*L.A. Co. Fire photo*

Developed during the middle 60's by the Thiokal Co., this "Snowcat" type vehicle, nick-named the "Sprite", was used to haul 400' of 1-1/2" hose and 800' of 1" hose up steep hills and other difficult terrain. The coming of the larger Bell 204 model helicopters beginning in 1967 usurped the function of this machine.

*Larry Arnold collection*

Many pieces of F & FW fire equipment may be viewed in this aerial shot of old Fire Station 44 being used as a staging area during the Fish Fork in 1953. (Can you spot the "Bathtub" Nashes?)

B. N. Landrum photo

The fuel tender for the helicopters was stationed for many years at Station 47 in Temple City. This 1968 Ford held 1,000 gallons of JP 4 fuel.

Larry Arnold Collection

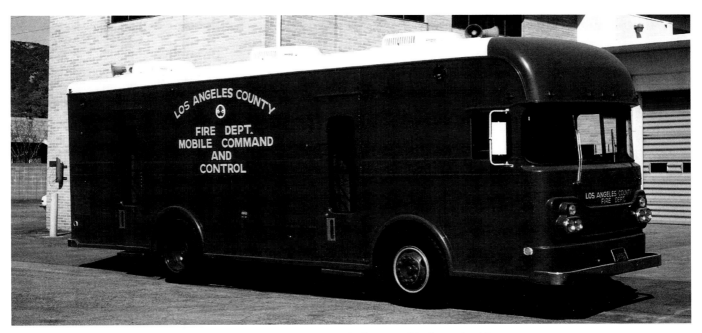

Built by Grumman/Gestenschlager on a 1965 International chassis, this large-incident command van features internal synthesizer radio system as well as the normal command and tactical frequencies. It is powered by an 8.2 GMC turbo diesel.

*Larry Cummings photo*

Supervisor Dean Dana, Capt. John Hunter and "Theo" pose with Catalina Station 55's 1979 Chevrolet Patrol, a typical one-ton unit with 125 G.P.M. power take off pump and 100 gallon tank. Stokes Litter rescue basket is mounted on top of storage cabinet behind Theo.

*Catalina "Islander" photo, courtesy Rick Harp*

This 1956 photo shows the Utility Driver from Bn. 8 H.Q. and his Ford F-350 pickup performing routine annual hydrant maintenance.

*L.A. Co. Fire photo*

The first Rescue Squad in the Crescenta-Cañada Valley was this spiffy 1956 Ford F-100 half-ton panel truck responding out of Station 19. E-19's new Crown, left.

*L.A. County Fire photo*

# VI Contemporary Apparatus 1972-1995

Even as many Crown Coach pumpers, snorkels and squirts continued to be purchased in the early 1970's, the large fleet of 1954 though 1956 Crowns and all the 1949 General Pacifics and 1950–52 International pumpers began to require immediate replacement. The same could be said for the first-generation American La France and Seagrave ladder trucks. They were replaced in small groups by American La France rear-mounted aerials.

In 1971, a large amount of money was set aside for the replacement of 46 pumpers, the largest order placed up to that time. Competitive bids were let in the fall, and a contract was signed with the Ward La France Company of Elmira Heights, New York, to

One of four 1974 Crown 1,000 G.P.M. pumpers with 500 gallon water tanks delivered in 1974, this one to F.S. 69 in Topanga Canyon, Malibu. Others went to F.S. 66, Altadena; F.S. 68, Calabassas, and F.S. 76, Castaic.

*C. Madderom photo*

One of eight 1974 Ward La France 1,000 G.P.M. pumpers with 500 gallon tanks delivered to L.A. County, this one to F.S. 81 in Mint Canyon. (Shop #49607)

*C. Madderom photo*

The companion apparatus to Engine 81 was this 1973 Ford Patrol on a Ford 1-ton chassis. This typical County Patrol has a 125 G.P.M. Power take-off pump, a bin with 300' of 1" cotton-jacketed hose and a 100 gallon water tank.

*C. Madderom photo*

This lighting unit was built on a 1974 Ford flatbed and chassis, and is stationed at Station 103, Pico-Rivera.

*C. Madderom photo*

manufacture and deliver the units to Los Angeles County at a per-unit cost of $44,000. In addition, a factory representative/mechanic was assigned to live in Los Angeles to supervise the delivery and acceptance tests and provide general factory/Los Angeles County public relations. Delivery of all 46 units was complete by the fall of 1972.

Specifications for the 46 pumpers included 1,500 G.P.M. single-stage Waterous main pumps rated at 1,000 G.P.M., 500 gallon capacity water tanks, a single hose reel plumbed to a High Fog high-pressure pump on the District rigs, and two hose reels for cotton-jacketed brush hose for the Forester and Fire Warden rigs. All featured the Allison HT-70 automatic transmission.

Assignments of the Ward La France units were to the Consolidated Fire Protection District as Engines 3, 5, 9, 12, 19, 29, 30, 33, 37, 40, 41, 43, 53, 71, 83, 87, 90, 96, 98, 111, 115, 116, 141, 145, 146, 273, and 282. Forester and Fire Warden units were assigned as Engines 46, 62, 64, 65, 67, 70, 72, 74, 78, 79, 81, 97, 99, 123, 125, and 325.

The initial success of these engines prompted the ordering of eight more for the 1974 delivery. They were initially assigned as Engines 46, 63, 75, 81, 86, 102, 129, and 307. This caused three of the higher-mileaged 1972 models to be moved to reserve status as Engines 507, 518, and 539.

The configuration of the cabs on the 1972 and 1974 Ward La France engines became the first indication of the eventual complete enclosing of the engine's crew within the cab. An engine crew of three, which was the standard in about half of the Department at that time, could easily fit on the three forward-facing seats found within the wide cab. Thus, the crew received protection from inclement weather during long responses and during long move-ups ,which, in some areas, might have reached 50 miles or more.

Cabs on units delivered in 1994 and beyond are completely enclosed and include air conditioning, even for the four-man crews utilizing the rear-facing jump seats. This is also an area for escape if the engine and crew were to be overrun during a fast-moving wildland fire.

Since the early 1980's, many other improvements have been added gradually. Features such as a shorter turning radius, larger wheels and tires, pre-plumbed Stang monitors, intra-cab communication devices for the entire crew, and a return to the standard transmission, normally a Spicer 6 forward speed model.

The rest of this book is devoted to "modern era"

apparatus, generally from 1972 to 1995. Suitable data on each equipment type will be found adjacent to the equipment presented or in captions found under individual photographs.

When looking back to the District's towed fire trailers of 1920 and the converted tree-watering trucks of the Forester and Fire Warden department, one can easily see and appreciate the enormous advances made in power, speed, maneuverability, load carrying capacity and, above all, safety—all of which have been made during the 75-year history of the Los Angeles County Fire Department.

It may also be interesting to note the difference in size and price between present-day apparatus and the first rigs ordered by the Districts and Forester and Fire Warden in the mid 1920's. No attempt has been made to furnish prices charged for the apparatus presented throughout the book, but a first and last listing might be interesting.

For the sake of comparison, look at the first District apparatus ordered in 1923–24. They were priced $10,000 to $12,500, and, depending on the make, had two-wheel mechanical brakes, weighed 5–8 tons

and had engines delivering less than 100 horsepower. The most recent pumper purchased in 1995 was made by KME, cost $232,238, has four-wheel air brakes, weighs 16 tons, has an engine that delivers 375 horsepower, and, of course, has an enclosed cab with air conditioning.

A few more amazing figures: a 1993 100 ft. aerial ladder truck with 425 horsepower engine at a cost of $520,398; $441,383 for Truck 187's two-axle Quint; and $452,665 for Truck 33's three-axle Quint. Both Quints have 425 horsepower Caterpillar engines.

As stated elsewhere, it will be fascinating to see what fire trucks of the future are able to do. Perhaps they will be somewhat smaller and/or more specialized in Los Angeles County. It is doubtful that they will be all Quints (as is currently the case in St. Louis, Missouri), for our territorial demands are too varied, even extreme. In any event, the day of the million-dollar pumper may not be far off. Are we ready for that?

And so it goes.

One of the 1961 Ford/Sabco Brush units as updated with an International cab and chassis, diesel engine and fully enclosed jump seats for the crew. These units are now completely out of service.

*C. Madderom photo*

The 1970 Crown 1,500 G.P.M. pumper with 300 gallon tank delivered to South Gate Station 52. This apparatus featured a 54' Telesquirt boom for fast elevated attack (#1660).

C. Madderom photo

A refurbished Engine 254, formerly Engine 52, in service at Southgate Station 54 (See photo above).

C. Madderom photo

One of five 1977 Crown 1,250 pumpers with 500 gallon tank made for L.A. County. Crown #F1783 was equipped with an 855 Cummins diesel engine and given to Station 31, Paramount.

*C. Madderom photo*

Part of the great 46-rig fleet delivered to L.A. County in 1972 was Pearblossom Engine 279. This Ward La France came with an 855 Cummins diesel and two hose reels supplied by a 500 gallon tank delivered by a Waterous 1,000 (rated) G.P.M. pump.

*C. Madderom photo*

1,300 gallon Water Tender 80, Acton, poses for the camera at the rear of the station. This 1973 Ford/Klein is now in reserve (#45411).

*C. Madderom photo*

Normally at Pacoima Warehouse, this 1975 International/Klein 1,675 gallon tanker is in quarters at F.S. 73, Newhall (#40213).

*C. Madderom photo*

Still sporting its Bicentennial wheels, Tanker 73, Newhall, a 1974 GMC/Klein with 1,675 gallon tank, poses in front of the station.

*C. Madderom photo*

Engine 62's 1972 Ward La France was delivered to the original Forestry Station in Padua Hills whose low door opening required a depressed light bar and monitor.

*C. Madderom photo*

A special order 1973 Ward La France delivered to Universal Studios for use in the famous "Emergency" TV series. This was housed at Universal, and is now at Yosemite National Park (WLF #80-811).

*C. Madderom photo*

One of the 22 such American La France 1,000 G.P.M. (rated) pumpers with 500 gallon tanks and 855 Cummins diesel engines delivered to L.A. County in 1981, ending a four-year period when very few pumpers were purchased (Co. #49419). The other assignments were as follows: Station 95 in Compton, 28 in Whittier, 20 in Norwalk, 56 in Palos Verdes, 163 in Bell, 61 in Walnut, 39 in Bell Gardens, 37 in Palmdale, 165 in Southgate, 23 in Bellflower, 49 in La Mirada, 41 in Willowbrook, 151 in Glendora, 21 in Lawndale, 84 in Quartz Hill, 3 in East Los Angeles, 18 in Lennox, 35 in Cerritos, 83 Palos Verdes, 110 in Marina Del Rey, 22 in Commerce, and 27 in Commerce.

*L. Arnold photo*

This 1980 Chevrolet Paramedic Squad was one of the last to not have the four-door sedan cab. A few sedan-cabbed units were purchased for stations having Paramedic trainees assigned.

*C. Madderom photo*

Squad 90 was (and is) one of the busier squads and qualified for a sedan-cabbed unit to haul trainees, such as this 1981 Chevrolet.

*C. Madderom photo*

By the middle 80's, a complete switch to sedan-cabbed squads had been made. Here, Azusa Squad 32 shows off its 1987 GMC unit with new-style light bar, quartz incident ground illumination lights and auxiliary red lights on the front bumper.

*C. Madderom photo*

Four of these 1971 American La France 100' Aerials replaced some of the older American La France and Seagrave Aerials from the 50's and early 60's. In addition to Truck 28, Whittier, shown here (#2536) assignments were to stations 42 in Rosemead, 20 in Norwalk, and 45 in Lakewood.

*C. Madderom photo*

Five of these American La France rear mount 100' Aerials (Century models) were delivered to L.A. County in 1977. They differed from the 1971 models in that they had dual rear axles. Assignments were as follows: Station 3 in East Los Angeles, 164 in Huntington Park, 116 in Carson, 106 in Rolling Hills, and shown, 30 in Cerritos (#CE-35-4821).

*C. Madderom photo*

A 1988 two-for-one shot showing Station 50's (Commerce) 1980 Crown 1,000 G.P.M. Telesquirt (50') with 500 gallon tank, and the 1976 Crown pumper with 1,000 G.P.M. pump and 500 gallon tank. Engine 250 has recently been replaced with a Paramedic Squad.

*L. Arnold photo*

A slightly different 1981 American La France Century Series pumper in that it has kept its hard suctions and has modified front red warning light system.

*C. Madderom photo*

Malibu's 1989 Seagrave 50' Tele-squirt features a 1500 G.P.M. pump and a 500 gallon tank. It is one of 4 such units spotted around the county.

*Kenneth Morris photo*

A 1985 photo of Engine 254, formerly Engine 52, a 1971 Crown Telesquirt (50') (Ex South Gate Engine 1) Crown #F1660, Co. #49004.

*L. Arnold photo*

Taken in 1980, this photo shows the original configuration of Engine 73, a 1976 Crown 1,000 G.P.M. pumper with 500 gallon tank (Co. #49617). Total refurbishing with new red light system occurred in 1990. It is now in reserve.

*L. Arnold photo*

Here sporting the then-new style light bar, Duarte Engine 44 poses for the camera. This 1976 Crown (F-1765) had the standard 1,000 G.P.M. (rated) pump and 500 gallon tank with a Cummins 855 diesel engine.

*W. Hattersly photo*

Inherited when Palos Verdes contracted with L.A. County in 1988, this 1979 Crown (#F1818) boasted a 1,500 gallon pump, a 500 gallon tank, and a 568 Detroit diesel (49751).

*L. Arnold photo*

A newly refurbished 1984 Mack 1,500 G.P.M. pumper/tanker with Class "B" foam proportioner. This rig is leased from Shell Oil Co. and will be assigned somewhere in Bn 6, Canyon Country / Valencia / Newhall. No number has been assigned.

*Larry Cummings photo*

Here we see the unit Ford assigned to large incidents to provide extra equipment and medical aid to the fire fighters at the scene. It is manned as needed.

*C. Madderom photo*

Nicknamed "Wally Wagons," GMC Suburbans such as San Dimas Bn 2's 1991 unit serve as field Battalion Chief's rolling command centers. 5.9 turbo-charged Cummins diesel engines and all-wheel drive are featured.

*Larry Cummings photo*

This brand new 1994 GMC Suburban serves newly created Battalion 15 in the Pomona area. The newest such units come with 6.5 turbo-charged diesels.

*Larry Cummings photo*

Mobile apparatus repair vehicles serve one or more Battalions each throughout the department. Central San Gabriel Valley's Repair 10 uses the 1995 Dodge 3500 RAM with 5.9 turbo diesel engine.

*Larry Cummings photo*

Each of the construction camps has a myriad of specialized equipment attached to it. This 1991 GMC Topkick diesel dump truck belongs to Camp #2 in La Cañada-Flintridge in the middle of Bn. 4.

*Larry Cummings photo*

This Ford 7000 diesel unit serves the county out of Camp 2 as the Demolition Unit, having air-operated hammers and tools on board (49958).

*Larry Cummings photo*

Two views of the "Mobile Air" unit serving the department out of F.S. 115 in S. Whittier. This 1991 White/GMC features a computerized panel, 100 pre-filled air bottles, and 500 lbs. of air storage.

*Larry Cummings photo*

Water Tender 32 out of Azusa Station 32 is this 1975 GMC. This rather austere unit features a 2,000 gallon water tank.

*Larry Cummings photo*

This 1990 International Water Tender, #117 (formerly #33 quartered at F.S. 33), operates out of Station 117 east of Palmdale/Lancaster. It features a 2,000 gal. water tank, 500 G.P.M. pump, all-wheel drive, and weighs 52,000 lbs loaded.

*Larrt Cummings photo*

Urban Search & Rescue (USAR) unit 3 was the original USAR 1 pending the building of their present unit. This unit is on a 1990 Ford F-700 cab and chassis.

*Larry Cummings photo*

This 1989 GMC 5-ton flatbed/stakeside was originally used as USAR 1. It is now USAR 2. (34703).

*C. Madderom photo*

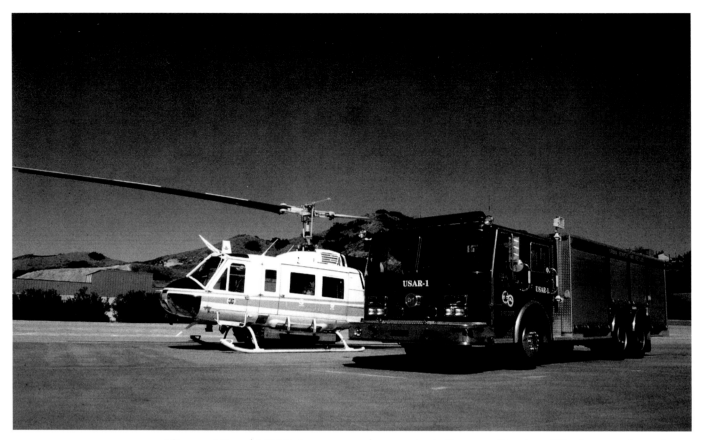

'Copter 15 and USAR 1 pose together on the heliport at Pacoima Warehouse where they are located together.

*Kenneth Morris photo*

Urban Search & Rescue Vehicle 1 on display at Klinger Center in 1994. Built on a 1992 Spartan cab & chassis, this 18-ton unit features storage body work by Supervac and a 400 H.P. Cummins diesel. It carries a 12 K Generator, 50 amp cutting torch and a 185 CFM Sullar air compressor.

*D. Boucher photo*

South Central Los Angeles' E-241's 1993 KME 1,000 G.P.M. (rated) pumper with 500 gallon tank is shown in normal and engine inspection mode. These units feature fully enclosed air conditioned cabs, class "A" foam proportioners, and a 375 H.P. Caterpillar diesel engine (Co. #F0177)

*D. Boucher photos*

Lancaster's brand new 1995 KME 1,000 G.P.M. rated triple-combination pumper is one of three recently delivered to that city.

*Larry Cummings photo*

Delivered along with Lancaster's 3 new pumpers was this 1995 "Quint" by KME. It features a 435 Caterpillar diesel, 1,000 G.P.M. rated pump and 75' aerial ladder.

*Larry Cummings photo*

All the new Lancaster pumper and ladder equipment poses near new (replacement) fire
station 129.

*Larry Cummings photo*

The balance of equipment responding at Lancaster Station 129 is shown: Water tender,
tractor with lowboy & bulldozer, Battalion Chief's Suburban, Paramedic Squad, EST
Engine and Engine 129 itself, a 1988 KME. The Bell Jet Ranger 'Copter is available for
the entire Department.

*Larry Cummings photo*

Transport 7's Mack tractor is hooked up to pull the L.A. County F.D. "mother" tanker, a 6,500 gallon behemoth used to resupply distant construction camps, reservoirs, extended fires, and other disasters (49806).

*Chuck Madderom photo*

This one-of-a-kind experiment for Los Angeles County is a 1993 Freightliner, in service as Engine 79, Bn 11 serving the desert areas of Pearblossom/Valjermo. This is the first unit delivered to L.A. Co. to use the roll-up cabinet doors. It features a 1,000 G.P.M. main pump and a 500 gallon tank.

*Larry Cummings photo*

Pomona Station 185 sports this brand new 1995 Ford F-350 with turbo-charged diesel engine as its Paramedic Squad.

The Ladder Co. inherited from Pomona is this 1985 Seagrave articulated 100' aerial.

All of the new Battalion 15 consists of the city of Pomona, and with the contract L.A. Co. inherited a fleet of Mack pumpers, the first in the department since 1950. Here Engine 188's 1974 CF model with a 1,500 G.P.M. pump and 500 gallon tank is shown.

*Larry Cummings photo*

This 1989 Mack/Westate 1,500 G.P.M. pumper with 500 gallon tank is found at Station 182, Pomona.

*Larry Cummings photo*

Transport 3's Mack tractor with Caterpillar D-8 Tractor with bulldozer parked in front of
F.S. 125 awaits a brush fire response.

*Larry Cummings photo*

The Department's Caterpillar road grader parked near F.S. 125. This is used extensively
for construction projects and for opening fire control motorways prior to each summer's
fire season.

*Larry Cummings photo*

Helitender 5's International tanker (CT20033) in front of F.S. 74 awaits a brush response where it will refuel helicopters in the field with JP 4 fuel.

*C. Madderom photo*

Truck 8 in West Hollywood received this 1973 American La France Pacemaker 100' rear mount aerial (21-309).

*C. Madderom photo*

When F.S. 57 in Norwood Village was closed in 1976, its 1965 Crown pumper with 1,250 main pump and 500 gallon tank was bumped down to F.S. 4 in South San Gabriel (49212).

*L. Arnold photo.*

Formerly Engine 214 in Watts, this 1976 Crown with 1,250 pump and 500 gallon tank was bumped down to F.S. 60 at the Universal Studios, replacing their open-cabbed 1965 Crown (49368).

*L. Arnold photo*

First built for a TV series, this 1976 GMC/Emergency 1 4 x 4 quick-attack pumper was actually considered to be a large brush patrol vehicle, and was assigned to old Station 77 at Quail Lake, east of Gorman. It was reassigned to F.S. 55 on Catalina Island. It features a 250 G.P.M. main pump and a 300 gallon tank (49627).

*L. Arnold photo*

The 1,800 gallon tanker assigned to F.S. 33 in Lancaster. This 1974 GMC bore Co. #(46439).

*L. Arnold photo*

The second and current platform for Deluge 87 is this 1984 GMC. The Intelligiant
Deluge Set remains unchanged.

*C. Madderom photo*

Shown here in its retracted position, light unit 52, Southgate, is mounted on a 1981
Chevrolet 1-1/2 ton cab and chassis.

*C. Madderom photo*

A typical current style Squad with a sedan cab is this 1988 GMC/Phoenix unit assigned to F.S. 101 in Claremont (F00010).

*L. Arnold photo*

A 1989 GMC Squad, very similar to the '88 models, shows improved red warning lights and a pre-positioned quartz light for working ground illumination. Squad 36 is located in Carson.

*C. Madderom photo*

Copter 18, one of the newest deliveries to the L.A. County helicopter fleet of six first-line units, on display at H.Q. This twin-engine Bell model 412 is fitted for both Air Squad and water-dropping roles.

*D. Boucher photo*

'Copter 18, one of the new Bell 412 machines, lands at an unknown helispot to take on 360 gallons of water.

*Ken Morris photo*

Bell Jet Ranger Helicopter 10, a Bell 206B, in its down position at Barton Heliport adjacent to the Pacoima Warehouse.

*D. Boucher photo*

'Copters 16, 18, and 15 in line in their down position at Barton Heliport, December of 1994. Copter 18 is the newest (a Bell 412) twin-engined model from Bell Aircraft.

*D. Boucher photo*

Similar to 'Copters 15 and 16, 'Copter 14, A Bell 205A-1, in its down position at Barton Heliport. Note parts craft against fence, right center.

*D. Boucher photo*

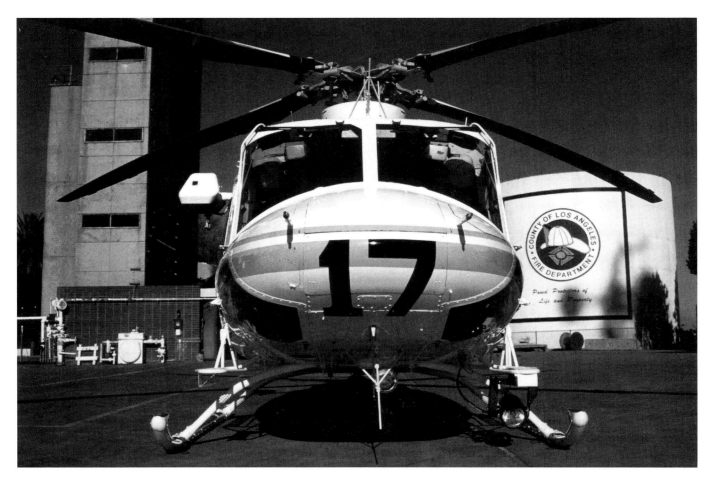

A beautiful head-on view of the Bell Model 412 'copter which is 'Copter 17. It poses here at the H.Q. training center without its drop tank.

*Larry Cummings photo*

Two of these Canada Air CL-215Y "Super Scoopers" will be leased for the next 5 years under a special appropriation by the L.A. Co. Board of Supervisors. Based at Van Nuys Airport, they will respond to brush fires throughout the county. The plane can scoop 1,410 gallons of water into its tank in 10 seconds on a smooth or small-wave water surface. It also features a foam proportioner adjacent to the water tank.

*Canada Air photo*

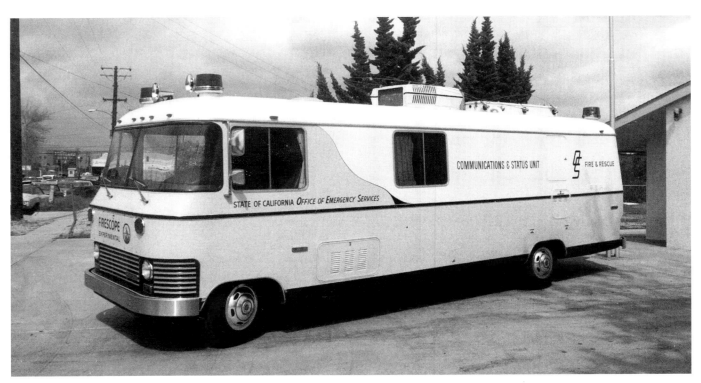

The State of California Office of Emergency Services has assigned the Communications and Status Unit (Comstatt 6) to L.A. Co. for use on multi-agency fires.

*L. Cummings photo*

The working end of a slip-on hot food delivery unit out of Fire Camp 2. From this unit flows beef, potatoes, green beans, bread and butter, coffee and juice for 100 hungry fire fighters during extended brush fires.

*D. Boucher photo*

Although plain in appearance, the 1994 Ford Victoria H. Q. Staff car carries a complete range of communication equipment for the Chief Officer on board.

*D. Boucher photo*

A brand new GMC Top Kick Camp Crew truck standing by at Pacoima Warehouse while its crew works inside. These all-wheel drive diesel-powered units offer complete protection for their 10-man crew. The Foreman's fire clothes hang on the side near the door.

*D. Boucher photo*

On display at H.Q., brand new 'Dozer 6 on its lowboy is the very latest in power and protection. This model D-8N International/Loadstar also features a completely enclosed air-conditioned cab (F40219).

*L. Cummings photo*

1995 Dodge Ram Dozer Tender 11 poses next to its charge, a brand new D-8N Dozer 6 by International/Loadstar.

*L. Cummings photo*

San Dimas Engine 264's 1995 KME 1,000 G.P.M. (rated) pumper in the early afternoon light. It features a 375 H.P. Caterpillar diesel engine and a 500 gallon tank.

*L. Cummings photo*

Operating in the center of the refining district in the City of Carson, Foam 10 operates this 1991 KME 2,000 G.P.M. pumper/tanker for use during petro-chemical incidents. It features a 1,750 ATC foam tank, a 250 gallon spare tank, and a 2,000 G.P.M. pre-plumbed monitor (F0062).

*C. Madderom photo*

The Forestry section uses this 1973 International "Hydro Seeder" to pump a mixture of water, seed, and mulch onto newly burned slopes—in order to prevent erosion—from it's 1,300 gallon tank.

*L. Cummings photo*

This 1990 GMC/Grumann van with 8.2 GMC diesel and Allison automatic transmission serves as Haz Mat 87. Haz Mat 76 and 105 have similar equipment.

*Larry Cummings photo*

As a result of absorbing the L.A. County Lifeguards in July of 1994, the Department added this 1994 Ford Ranger XLT, plus six others, and this 32' Seaway patrol boat, Model 6 BTA. It is powered by a 5.9 300 H.P. diesel engine and has a top speed of 40 MPH. Quartered at Marina Del Rey, it is very near the Department's fireboat. It is also equipped with Radar, direction finder, Loran and VHF and department radios, as well as a 125 G.P.M. fire pump.

*Tom Estlow photo*

L.A. County Lifeguards get first water on this burning sloop in Santa Monica Bay

*Tom Estlow collection*

One of five such specialized units, EST 145 is a 1992 Ford/La Grange 100 G.P.M. pumper with a 150 gallon tank. The Darley pump also pumps through a class "A" or "B" foam proportioner.

*L. Cummings photo*

In order to pull the USAR trailers and haul the Battalion air cache, certain Battalion Utility trucks have received these 1995 GMC 1-1/2 ton stakeside units with lift gates. Bn. 4's unit is shown here at Station 82.

*D. Boucher photo*

Constructed in the 1950's to replace the forestry command trailer found on page 28, this combination dispatching/H.Q. trailer is kept in readiness at the Pacoima Warehouse for use on large extended brush fires.

*D. Boucher photo*

Completed last year, this trailer hauls all types of gear for use during large river/flood rescue efforts (F8002).

*D. Boucher photo*

# VII Where Are They Now?

The decision to retire a piece of fire apparatus in Los Angeles County is based on both age and condition, and much of the condition is based on mileage shown on the odometer. In most cases, apparatus is used in a standby or reserve capacity before it is placed on the auction block. The auction block in Los Angeles County is in the form of a sealed bid, and has been the source of many a fire engine for a smaller town somewhere in the West. With minor to major refurbishing, some of these rigs with far lower emergency demands can last in another jurisdiction for many years after they can no longer withstand the rigors of the heavy use of the Los Angeles County Fire Department.

Over the years, since World War II, dozens of worn but still serviceable pumpers and tankers have been given to small towns in Mexico as part of the "Bomberos" program active within the Los Angeles County Fire Department. Mack, Seagrave, and currently Ward La France apparatus have been driven or hauled across the border by groups of off-duty fire fighters and other interested parties. The hospitality afforded these men has been reported as outstanding upon their arrival in the town receiving the engines.

A few "previously owned" apparatus are pictured and described in this section. We know there are many more of them out there and that we will be informed about them as soon as this book is published. (That seems to be the way things work out when researching for the writing of any book.)

Four barely serviceable 1972 Ward La France pumpers await their last assignment as Training Rigs 1, 2, 3, and 4, here at Klinger Center drill grounds for new recruits. They have come from ready reserve status, and will be sold to the highest bidder or sent to salvage from this assignment.

*D. Boucher photo*

One of six Stutz 450 G.P.M. pumpers, which were original Fire district equipment in 1924, sits in rough but restorable condition behind a storage building. A sister rig is owned by the L.A. County Fire Museum Association.

*Larry Arnold photo*

A tired but intact 1924 REO-Obenchain-Boyer waiting to be sold behind the Pacoima Warehouse. This rig was original Flintridge equipment, then sold in 1930 to Lancaster F.P.D., and was finally Engine 84 in Quartz Hill, an amazing record for such a small and underpowered 350 G.P.M. pumper. It now belongs to the L.A. Co. Fire Museum.

*George Bass photo*

Altadena Station 11 first claimed this 1924 American La France chain drive type 750 pumper, installed when the station opened. It is pictured here in Verdi, Nevada, where its rotary pump is put to good use at this high elevation by the volunteers.

*Larry Arnold photo*

High on a roof in Vernon, California, perches this 1949 General Pacific 1,000 G.P.M. pumper, one of nine purchased for L.A. County. It was sold to Harmony, California, in 1972, and re-purchased for display on this roof (49060).

*L. Arnold Photo*

Originally Engine 382 (49539), this 1957 FWD/Yankee/Calavar 750 G.P.M. pumper with a 500 gallon tank was sold about 1970 to Big Bear Lake, California, and painted yellow.

*Larry Arnold photo*

1968 Crown Reserve E-555 reaches the end of the line at the Pacoima Warehouse boneyard after recently suffering serious radiated heat damage (49586).

*D. Boucher photo*

Cathedral City, California became the proud owner of this 1956 Crown 1,250 G.P.M. pumper with 500 gallon tank (F-1061), (49128). The cab was enclosed by L.A. County in the early 70's.

*L. Arnold photo*

Shown here in reserve prior to being sold is the former Engine 80, Acton, with its new number, Engine 539. This 1963 model Crown featured a sedan cab, 1,250 G.P.M. main pump and a 500 gallon water tank.

*Larry Arnold photo*

A very recent photo (1994) of F.S. 60's 1,250 G.P.M. Crown on display for the Fire Buff's convention at Klinger Center (H.Q.). This rig is now the property of the L.A. Co. Museum Association. Station 60 has been renumbered Station 51.

*David Boucher photo*

One of three 1950 Mack pumper/tankers purchased for Stations 66(E-85), 69, and 46, this unit is presently being restored by L.A. Co. Captain Robert Hewitt of Station 47A.

*Robert Hewitt collection*

Where old fire engines go: the boneyard at the Pacoima Warehouse. Here two Camp Crew trucks, a 1966 Crown Snorkel and a 1974 Ward La France pumper await disposal or use for spare parts.

*D. Boucher photo*

Originally Engine 17 in Santa Fe Springs, this 1929 Seagrave 1,000 G.P.M. pumper retired to Station 27 and then short-lived Station 108. Here it awaits its fate at the Pacoima Warehouse in 1951.

*Shaun Ryan collection*

On August 3, 1948 Engine 54's 1924 American La France met with an early termination when it collided with a truckload of structural steel at Western Ave. and Florence Blvd. Miraculously, no deaths occurred.

*L.A. Co. Fire photo*

One of two wartime deliveries to L.A. County was this 1942 Ford La France 500 G.P.M. pumper with 400 gallon tank. Presently owned by Keith Gustavson, an L.A. Co. Engineer, it originally served as either Engine 68, Calabassas, or Engine 83, Miraleste (Palos Verdes).

*K. Gustavson photo*

Owned by L.A. County Engineer Tom Tibbett, this 1931 Moreland, Pumper J, was recently relocated in a garage in Station 157's district of Green Valley. About $25,000 should take care of its restoration.

*D. Boucher photo*

The 1924 REO-Obenchain-Boyer pumper first purchased for Flintridge E-28 awaits restoration in the L.A. Co. Fire Museum in Southgate.

*D. Boucher photo*

Fully restored original Engine 12, a 1928 Seagrave 750 pumper with F-6 engine, is parked on-line at the L.A. County Fire Museum in Southgate.

*D. Boucher photo*

# Epilogue

About the only certainty existing concerning the Los Angeles County Fire Department is that fluctuating periods of change will always be with us. Somewhat erratic funding sources create occasional periods of decreased manpower, temporary Engine Company or Station closures or realignments and reduction in numbers of replacement apparatus purchased. Then, as funding improves, more equipment is purchased and/or refurbished and manpower replaced. It would be safer to say that the Department has *about* 30 Truck Companies, 147 Engine Companies, 6 helicopters and tractors, etc., than to try to declare a fixed number, for as soon as a number is determined, it is soon changed.

A generally accepted figure for the area served by the Los Angeles County Fire Department has always been roughly 2,000 square miles. Yet, as recently as July 1, 1995, the City of Pomona elected to contract with Los Angeles County for fire protection, thereby adding 8 Stations housing 8 Engine Companies, 2 Ladder Companies and 2 Paramedic Squads to the roster, along with another 25 square miles. One of the Stations housing a truck will receive a new Quint (Station 187). Another Quint will be assigned to Station 33 in Lancaster. And so it goes.

Mechanically, 70 existing engines and all future engines will be retrofitted or equipped with Foampro 2001 foam proportioners, although no piece of equipment older than the 1981 American La Frances will qualify for this change. Monsanto Class "A" Foam WD881 will be the product of choice for use with these installations. Additionally, a return to the automatic transmission for future 1995–96 engine and truck deliveries is indicated. If the transmission of choice is equivalent to the Allison units used between 1968 and 1980, a long era of tranquility regarding transmission/clutch problems will be in order, not to mention an increase in the amount of attention paid to steering, braking, and traffic by the Engineer.

This has been the first complete apparatus book concerning the Los Angeles County Fire Department, and the last one to be attempted by this author. Another time, another person, ten or twenty years from now . . . what amazing changes will he or she write about? What a pleasure it will be to contemplate them.

# APPARATUS IDENTIFICATION

Several different lettering or numbering systems are used in this book to identify certain apparatus beyond the usual engine or truck company number. These are not always available for every apparatus, but when they are, one or more may be used in the photo captions. A summary of these systems is included here.

I. **Pumpers "A" through "W"**
A system of identifying the largest pumpers used by the Los Angeles County Forester and Fire Warden from 1929 until just prior to World War II. A shop number was also painted on each side of the apparatus.

II. **"N" number**
A system of identifying all apparatus in the Forester and Fire Warden Department from just prior to World War II until it was phased out in the late 1960's to early 70's. This was the shop number and was used in addition to the engine company number.

III. **"FD" number**
A system of identifying district apparatus (as opposed to Forester and Fire Warden apparatus) in use until phased out in the early 1970's in favor of the next system.

IV. **"49" number**
The FD number was replaced by the prefix 49 for all district apparatus only. If an apparatus did not have a 49 number, it was identified as belonging to the Forester and Fire Warden.

V. **"F-1069" (ex.)**
An F followed by a dash indicates a number assigned to a piece of Crown Coach (only) apparatus by the factory (only).

VI. **"F0045" (ex.)**
A number assigned to apparatus belonging to the entire Los Angeles County Fire Department purchased after the two sections of the Department were united in every aspect in October 1992. This system will replace the other systems as time progresses.

# CHRONOLOGY OF SIGNIFICANT APPARATUS PURCHASES

1909    First Fire Warden appointed by Los Angeles County Board of Supervisors. Fire Warden was also the Fish and Game Warden. No vehicle assigned.

1920    Fire Warden and Fish and Game reassigned to the Forestry Department. Vehicles inherited from Forestry included two used Ford Model T's and two Indian motorcycles. All vehicles were painted green.

1921    Forester and Fire Warden purchased two new Ford Model T's.

1922    Forester and Fire Warden purchased a Dodge Brothers screen truck for hauling supplies and conscripts. Also purchased a Dodge Brothers touring car.

1923    Forester and Fire Warden purchased its first large White cargo truck and a REO pick-up truck. Two White 600 gallon capacity tankers were ordered.

1924    First fire district pumping apparatus purchased, painted red. Thirteen American La France, six Stutz, and seven REO-Obenchain-Boyers were purchased, along with the first Harley Davidson patrol motorcycle (Co. 37).

1928    First Seagrave pumpers were purchased.

1929    First two White Forester and Fire Warden fire tanker/ pumpers purchased, pumpers "E" and "F".

1930    First bulldozer blade attached to Caterpillar 30 tractor; used on fire in Tapia Park. Nine Moreland Forester and Fire Warden tanker/pumpers purchased, pumpers "G" through "O".

1933    First Mack Forester and Fire Warden tanker/pumper purchased, pumper "P".

1934    Last White Forester and Fire Warden fire tanker/pumper purchased, pumper "Q".

1936   Last Moreland pumper purchased, pumper "R".

1938   First Seagrave V-12 pumpers purchased for Forester and Fire Warden, pumpers "S" through "W".

1939   2500 gallon capacity Seagrave tanker/pumper delivered to Norwalk Fire Protection District. Largest tanker in the western United States at the time. Last motorcycle purchased for the Forestry and Fire Warden. First Mack pumpers purchased for the districts, two E models.

1948   Forester and Fire Warden stations given numbers and organized into "Mountain Battalions." Balance of green Forestry apparatus still in service painted red. First new red Forester and Fire Warden apparatus delivered.

1949   Consolidated Fire Protection District was formed from several separate districts. First General Pacific pumpers ordered.

1950   First aerial ladder truck delivered to the districts, an 85 ft. mid-mount American La France to Hollywood Station 8.

1953   Forester and Fire Warden and Fire Protection Districts combined organizationally. Forester and Fire Warden Mountain Battalions disbanded and their engines renumbered. First Seagrave aerial purchased, an 85 ft. mid-mount for Station 23.

1954   First Crown Coach pumpers purchased. Forty units ordered for the districts and Forester and Fire Warden.

1957   First FWD pumpers delivered to Forester and Fire Warden, E-382 and 373. First Los Angeles County Fire Department helicopter purchased, a Bell Model 47-G2.

1965   First aerial platform (snorkel) purchased for Los Angeles County Fire Department, a Crown Pittman 75 ft. model assigned to Truck 43.

1967   First large Bell 10-place helicopter purchased.

1968   First Crown Coach with diesel engine (855 Cummins) purchased for Forester and Fire Warden (F-1553). Switch made to automatic transmissions.

1972   All apparatus purchased from this time on delivered with a closed cab for riot and brush fire protection. Older open cab models had fiberglass cabs added. 46 Ward La France pumpers ordered. Department switched from aerial platforms to rear-mount aerial ladder trucks.

1981   Twenty-two American La France pumpers purchased, the first since 1941. Switch made back to manual transmissions.

1985   Twenty-one Van Pelt pumpers purchased.

1988   Eight KME pumpers purchased.

1989   First tillered 100 ft. aerials purchased, five from Seagrave.

1991   Sixteen Pierce pumpers purchased.

1992   First Freightliner pumper purchased, for Engine 79.

1995   First Quints purchased, two from KME, for Trucks 33 and 187.

---

NOTE: KME pumpers delivered in 1995 have fully enclosed air-conditioned cabs. Future pumper deliveries will have automatic transmissions. The total number of 100 ft. tillered aerials in service is currently eleven; one was inherited with the contracting of the City of Pomona in July 1995.

# PIERCE ENGINE ASSIGNMENTS

| VEH # | YEAR | MAKE | TYPE | ENGINE* | PUMP** | ASSIGNMENT |
|-------|------|------|------|---------|--------|------------|
| 49692 | 1991 | PIERCE | PUMPER | CATERPILLAR | 1000 GPM | ENGINE 307 |
| F0082 | 1991 | PIERCE | PUMPER | CATERPILLAR | 1000 GPM | ENGINE 053 |
| F0083 | 1991 | PIERCE | PUMPER | CATERPILLAR | 1000 GPM | ENGINE 106 |
| F0084 | 1991 | PIERCE | PUMPER | CATERPILLAR | 1000 GPM | ENGINE 141 |
| F0085 | 1991 | PIERCE | PUMPER | CATERPILLAR | 1000 GPM | ENGINE 146 |
| F0086 | 1991 | PIERCE | PUMPER | CATERPILLAR | 1000 GPM | ENGINE 073 |
| F0087 | 1991 | PIERCE | PUMPER | CATERPILLAR | 1000 GPM | ENGINE 031 |
| F0088 | 1991 | PIERCE | PUMPER | CATERPILLAR | 1000 GPM | ENGINE 020 |
| F0089 | 1991 | PIERCE | PUMPER | CATERPILLAR | 1000 GPM | ENGINE 122 |
| F0090 | 1991 | PIERCE | PUMPER | CATERPILLAR | 1000 GPM | ENGINE 005 |
| F0091 | 1991 | PIERCE | PUMPER | CATERPILLAR | 1000 GPM | ENGINE 047 |
| F0092 | 1991 | PIERCE | PUMPER | CATERPILLAR | 1000 GPM | ENGINE 027 |
| F0093 | 1991 | PIERCE | PUMPER | CATERPILLAR | 1000 GPM | ENGINE 054 |
| F0094 | 1991 | PIERCE | PUMPER | CATERPILLAR | 1000 GPM | ENGINE 003 |
| F0095 | 1991 | PIERCE | PUMPER | CATERPILLAR | 1000 GPM | ENGINE 058 |
| F0096 | 1991 | PIERCE | PUMPER | CATERPILLAR | 1000 GPM | ENGINE 214 |

*350 HP DIESEL; **RATED

# KOVATCH PUMPER ASSIGNMENTS

| VEH # | YEAR | MAKE | TYPE | ENGINE* | PUMP** | ASSIGNMENT |
|-------|------|------|------|---------|--------|------------|
| 49670 | 1989 | KME | PUMPER | CATERPILLAR | 1000 GPM | ENGINE 062 |
| 49671 | 1989 | KME | PUMPER | CATERPILLAR | 1000 GPM | ENGINE 129 |
| 49788 | 1988 | KME | PUMPER | CATERPILLAR | 1000 GPM | ENGINE 001 |
| 49789 | 1988 | KME | PUMPER | CATERPILLAR | 1000 GPM | ENGINE 006 |
| 49790 | 1988 | KME | PUMPER | CATERPILLAR | 1000 GPM | ENGINE 014 |
| 49791 | 1988 | KME | PUMPER | CATERPILLAR | 1000 GPM | ENGINE 016 |
| 49792 | 1988 | KME | PUMPER | CATERPILLAR | 1000 GPM | ENGINE 024 |
| 49793 | 1989 | KME | PUMPER | CATERPILLAR | 1000 GPM | ENGINE 042 |
| 49794 | 1989 | KME | PUMPER | CATERPILLAR | 1000 GPM | ENGINE 145 |
| 49795 | 1988 | KME | PUMPER | CATERPILLAR | 1000 GPM | ENGINE 071 |
| 49796 | 1989 | KME | PUMPER | CATERPILLAR | 1000 GPM | ENGINE 101 |
| 49797 | 1989 | KME | PUMPER | CATERPILLAR | 1000 GPM | ENGINE 118 |
| 49798 | 1989 | KME | PUMPER | CATERPILLAR | 1000 GPM | ENGINE 144 |
| F0041 | 1990 | KME | PUMPER | CATERPILLAR | 1000 GPM | ENGINE 007 |
| F0042 | 1990 | KME | PUMPER | CATERPILLAR | 1000 GPM | ENGINE 019 |
| F0043 | 1990 | KME | PUMPER | CATERPILLAR | 1000 GPM | ENGINE 043 |
| F0044 | 1990 | KME | PUMPER | CATERPILLAR | 1000 GPM | ENGINE 048 |
| F0045 | 1990 | KME | PUMPER | CATERPILLAR | 1000 GPM | ENGINE 065 |
| F0046 | 1990 | KME | PUMPER | CATERPILLAR | 1000 GPM | ENGINE 096 |
| F0047 | 1990 | KME | PUMPER | CATERPILLAR | 1000 GPM | ENGINE 098 |
| F0048 | 1990 | KME | PUMPER | CATERPILLAR | 1000 GPM | ENGINE 103 |
| F0049 | 1990 | KME | PUMPER | CATERPILLAR | 1000 GPM | ENGINE 105 |
| F0050 | 1990 | KME | PUMPER | CATERPILLAR | 1000 GPM | ENGINE 130 |
| F0051 | 1990 | KME | PUMPER | CATERPILLAR | 1000 GPM | ENGINE 114 |
| F0052 | 1990 | KME | PUMPER | CATERPILLAR | 1000 GPM | ENGINE 121 |
| F0053 | 1990 | KME | PUMPER | CATERPILLAR | 1000 GPM | ENGINE 124 |
| F0054 | 1990 | KME | PUMPER | CATERPILLAR | 1000 GPM | ENGINE 131 |
| F0169 | 1993 | KME | PUMPER | CATERPILLAR | 1000 GPM | ENGINE 070 |
| F0170 | 1993 | KME | PUMPER | CATERPILLAR | 1000 GPM | ENGINE 097 |
| F0171 | 1993 | KME | PUMPER | CATERPILLAR | 1000 GPM | ENGINE 076 |
| F0172 | 1993 | KME | PUMPER | CATERPILLAR | 1000 GPM | ENGINE 087 |
| F0173 | 1993 | KME | PUMPER | CATERPILLAR | 1000 GPM | ENGINE 265 |
| 49174 | 1993 | KME | PUMPER | CATERPILLAR | 1000 GPM | ENGINE 018 |
| F0175 | 1993 | KME | PUMPER | CATERPILLAR | 1000 GPM | ENGINE 036 |
| F0176 | 1993 | KME | PUMPER | CATERPILLAR | 1000 GPM | ENGINE 037 |
| F0177 | 1993 | KME | PUMPER | CATERPILLAR | 1000 GPM | ENGINE 241 |
| F0309 | 1995 | KME | PUMPER | CATERPILLAR | 1000 GPM | ENGINE 021 |
| F0310 | 1995 | KME | PUMPER | CATERPILLAR | 1000 GPM | ENGINE 244 |
| F0311 | 1995 | KME | PUMPER | CATERPILLAR | 1000 GPM | ENGINE 033 |
| F0312 | 1995 | KME | PUMPER | CATERPILLAR | 1000 GPM | ENGINE 099 |
| F0313 | 1995 | KME | PUMPER | CATERPILLAR | 1000 GPM | ENGINE 208 |
| F0314 | 1995 | KME | PUMPER | CATERPILLAR | 1000 GPM | ENGINE 282 |
| F0315 | 1995 | KME | PUMPER | CATERPILLAR | 1000 GPM | ENGINE 149 |
| F0316 | 1995 | KME | PUMPER | CATERPILLAR | 1000 GPM | ENGINE 063 |
| F0317 | 1995 | KME | PUMPER | CATERPILLAR | 1000 GPM | ENGINE 264 |
| F0318 | 1995 | KME | PUMPER | CATERPILLAR | 1000 GPM | ENGINE 134 |
| F0319 | 1995 | KME | PUMPER | CATERPILLAR | 1000 GPM | ENGINE 135 |
| F0320 | 1995 | KME | PUMSPER | CATERPILLAR | 1000 GPM | ENGINE 125 |
| F0321 | 1995 | KME | PUMPER | CATERPILLAR | 1000 GPM | ENGINE 131 |
| F0322 | 1995 | KME | PUMPER | CATERPILLAR | 1000 GPM | ENGINE 273 |

*375 HP DIESEL; **RATED

# LOS ANGELES COUNTY FIRE DEPARTMENT—AERIALS

| VEH # | YEAR | MAKE | TYPE | ASSIGNMENT |
|-------|------|------|------|------------|
| 49205 | 1965 | CROWN | AERIAL 75 SNORKEL | TRUCK 568 |
| 49285 | 1973 | A/LAFR | AERIAL 100 R MT | TRUCK 004 |
| 49286 | 1971 | A/LAFR | AERIAL 100 R MT | TRUCK 513 |
| 49287 | 1971 | A/LAFR | AERIAL 100 R MT | TRUCK 504 |
| 49288 | 1971 | A/LAFR | AERIAL 100 R MT | TRUCK 033 |
| 49324 | 1973 | A/LAFR | AERIAL 100 R MT | TRUCK 110 |
| 49325 | 1973 | A/LAFR | AERIAL 100 R MT | TRUCK 515 |
| 49346 | 1977 | A/LAFR | AERIAL 100 R MT-TDM | TRUCK 125 |
| 49347 | 1977 | A/LAFR | AERIAL 100 R MT-TDM | TRUCK 086 |
| 49348 | 1977 | A/LAFR | AERIAL 100 R MT-TDM | TRUCK 116 |
| 49349 | 1977 | A/LAFR | AERIAL 100 R MT-TDM | TRUCK 106 |
| 49350 | 1977 | A/LAFR | AERIAL 100 R MT-TDM | TRUCK 030 |
| 49715 | 1966 | CROWN | AERIAL 75 SNORKEL-TDM | TRUCK 187 |
| 49717 | 1984 | V/PELT | AERIAL 100 PLATFORM-TDM | TRUCK 127 |
| 49718 | 1984 | V/PELT | AERIAL 100 PLATFORM-TDM | TRUCK 027 |
| 49779 | 1987 | LTI | AERIAL 108 R MT-TDM | TRUCK 049 |
| 49780 | 1987 | LTI | AERIAL 108 R MT-TDM | TRUCK 029 |
| 49781 | 1988 | LTI | AERIAL 108 R MT-TDM | TRUCK 073 |
| F0038 | 1989 | SEAGRAVE | AERIAL 100 TILLER | TRUCK 082 |
| F0039 | 1989 | SEAGRAVE | AERIAL 100 TILLER | TRUCK 008 |
| F0040 | 1989 | SEAGRAVE | AERIAL 100 TILLER | TRUCK 003 |
| F0056 | 1990 | SEAGRAVE | AERIAL 100 TILLER | TRUCK 028 |
| F0057 | 1990 | SEAGRAVE | AERIAL 100 TILLER | TRUCK 045 |
| F0179 | 1993 | LTI | AERIAL 100 TILLER | TRUCK 118 |
| F0180 | 1993 | LTI | AERIAL 100 TILLER | TRUCK 024 |
| F0181 | 1993 | LTI | AERIAL 100 TILLER | TRUCK 164 |
| F0182 | 1993 | LTI | AERIAL 100 TILLER | TRUCK 031 |
| F0183 | 1993 | LTI | AERIAL 100 TILLER | TRUCK 020 |
| F2021 | 1985 | SEAGRAVE | AERIAL 100 TILLER | TRUCK 181 |

P. Michael Freeman
*Fire Chief*

# COUNTY OF LOS ANGELES
# FIRE DEPARTMENT
# 1994
# STATISTICAL SUMMARY

### Mission Statement
*To proudly protect lives and property by providing prompt, skillful, cost-effective fire protection and life safety services.*

### County of Los Angeles Fire Department Provides Emergency Services For:

| | |
|---|---|
| 3,034,848 | Residents |
| 937,478 | Housing Units |
| 51 | Cities in the District |
| 2,257 | Total Square Miles |

DIVISION I
Batt's. 7, 14 (15 Stations)
(8 Cities)
  CARSON
  LAWNDALE
  LOMITA
  PALOS VERDES ESTATES
  RANCHO PALOS VERDES
  ROLLING HILLS
  ROLLING HILLS ESTATES
  SIGNAL HILL

DIVISION II
Batt's. 12, 16 (16 Stations)
(9 Cities)
  AZUSA
  BALDWIN PARK
  BRADBURY
  DIAMOND BAR
  DUARTE
  INDUSTRY
  LA PUENTE
  WALNUT
  IRWINDALE

DIVISION III
Batt's. 6, 11, 17 (25 Stations)
(3 Cities)
  LANCASTER
  PALMDALE
  SANTA CLARITA

DIVISION IV
Batt's. 8, 9 (17 Stations)
(9 Cities)
  ARTESIA
  BELLFLOWER
  CERRITOS
  HAWAIIAN GARDENS
  LAKEWOOD
  LA MIRADA
  NORWALK
  PARAMOUNT
  WHITTIER

DIVISION V
Batt's. 4, 10 (15 Stations)
(5 Cities)
  LA CANADA-
    FLINTRIDGE
  PICO RIVERA
  ROSEMEAD
  SOUTH EL MONTE
  TEMPLE CITY

DIVISION VI
Batt's. 3,13 (14 Stations)
(5 Cities)
  BELL
  BELL GARDENS
  COMMERCE
  CUDAHY
  HUNTINGTON PARK
  MAYWOOD
  SOUTH GATE

DIVISION VII
Batt's. 1, 5
(18 Stations)
(6 Cities)
  AGOURA HILLS
  CALABASAS
  HIDDEN HILLS
  MALIBU
  WEST HOLLYWOOD
  WESTLAKE VILLGE

DIVISION VIII
Batt's. 2, 15 (16 Stations)
(4 Cities)
  CLAREMONT
  GLENDORA
  POMONA
  SAN DIMAS

DIVISION III
Batt's. 6, 11, 17

DIVISION V
Batt's. 4, 10

DIVISION II
Batt's. 12, 16

DIVISION VIII
Batt's. 2, 15

DIVISION VII
Batt's. 1, 5

Santa Catalina Island

DIVISION VI
Batt's. 13, 3

DIVISION IV
Batt's. 8, 9

DIVISION I
Batt's. 7, 14

## BATTALION / DIVISION CONFIGURATION

# 1994 ACTIVITY SUMMARY

## Emergency Operations

| | |
|---|---|
| Fires | 11,219 |
| Rescues | 118,686 |
| Other | 60,099 |
| **Total Incidents** | **190,004** |
| Acres Burned | 6,897 |
| Fire Injuries | |
| Civilian | 32 |
| Fire Fighters | 11 |
| Fire Fatalities | |
| Civilian | 11 |
| Fire Fighters | 0 |
| Air Operations | |
| Fires | 536 |
| Rescues | 1,638 |
| Retardant Dropped (Gals.) | 1,898,113 |
| Passengers | 18,386 |
| Cargo (Pounds) | 316,236 |
| Health Hazard Incidents | 2,513 |

## Non-Emergency Operations

| | |
|---|---|
| Haz. Waste Inspections | 10,308 |
| Fire Prevention Inspections | 109,528 |
| Public Education | |
| Programs | 2,606 |
| Attendance | 2,327,488 |
| Forestry Activities | |
| Trees And Low-Fuel Plants | 60,748 |
| Programs And Inspections | 1,221 |
| Persons Served | 286,707 |

# FIVE YEAR DATA 1990-1994

| | 1994 | 1993 | 1992 | 1991* | 1990 |
|---|---|---|---|---|---|
| **Fire Incidents** | | | | | |
| Structures | 2,451 | 2,283 | 2,436 | 2,290 | 2,244 |
| Vehicles | 3,612 | 3,253 | 3,427 | 3,543 | 3,543 |
| Rubbish | 2,436 | 2,164 | 2,321 | 2,906 | 2,752 |
| Brush/Grass | 1,940 | 1,986 | 1,740 | 1,428 | 1,274 |
| Outside Storage | 519 | 422 | 456 | 39 | 29 |
| Misc. Property | 261 | 237 | 328 | 852 | 275 |
| *Total* | *11,219* | *10,345* | *10,708* | *11,058* | *10,117* |
| **EMS Incidents**\*\* | **118,686** | **118,117** | **117,301** | **125,662** | **129,228** |
| **Victims** | **122,140** | **123,119** | **125,512** | **134,459** | **138,274** |
| **Other Incidents** | | | | | |
| False Alarms | 37,319 | 35,810 | 7,431 | 3,006 | 5,302 |
| Smoke Scares | | | 1,820 | 1,441 | 4,038 |
| Vehicle Accidents | 6,125 | 5,386 | 5,047 | 2,954 | 2,509 |
| Misc. Non-Fire Inc. | 16,655 | 16,038 | 42,663 | 16,801 | 8,555 |
| *Total* | *60,099* | *57,234* | *56,961* | *24,202* | *20,404* |
| **All Incidents** | **190,004** | **185,696** | **184,970** | **169,719** | **168,795** |
| **Loss In Dollars** | | | | | |
| Improvements | $37,840,440 | $312,548,367 | $36,827,144 | $38,074,100 | $46,246,100 |
| Contents | 18,392,485 | 16,730,601 | 19,250,108 | 25,421,200 | 28,503,900 |
| Vehicle/Contents | 8,323,373 | 10,184,640 | 8,839,832 | 8,863,700 | 14,326,000 |
| Misc. Property | 1,541,806 | 1,899,860 | 3,186,798 | 4,099,200 | 6,033,000 |
| *Total* | *$66,098,104* | *$341,363,468* | *$68,103,882* | *$76,458,200* | *$95,109,000* |
| **Acreage Burned** | **6,897** | **30,664** | **2,569** | **2,466** | **1,401** |
| **Inspections** | | | | | |
| By Station | 79,924 | 75,813 | 75,786 | 73,267 | 74,088 |
| By Bureau | 29,604 | 34,340 | 39,979 | 40,008 | 39,897 |
| *Total* | *109,528* | *110,153* | *115,765* | *113,275* | *113,985* |

*Transition To CAD-Variations May Result

**March, 1993: EMS Information Retroactively Revised To Show Both Victim And Incident Information.

# DEPARTMENT RESOURCES

## Personnel

| | |
|---|---|
| Uniformed | |
| Chief Officers | 90 |
| Captains | 558 |
| FF Specialists | 700 |
| Fire Fighters | 1,130 |
| (Certified Paramedics—475) | |
| Foresters | 20 |
| *Total* | *2,498* |
| Dispatchers | 83 |
| Nonuniformed | 629 |
| Camps | |
| Fire Suppression Aides | 81 |
| (Inmates—560) | |
| (Wards—213) | |
| **Total Personnel** | **3,291** |

## Facilities

| | |
|---|---|
| Fire Stations | 136 |
| Fire Suppression Camps | |
| Paid | 3 |
| Inmates | 8 |
| *Total* | *11* |
| Fire Prevention Office | 14 |
| Forestry Nurseries | 7 |
| **Total Facilities** | **168** |

## Equipment

| | |
|---|---|
| Aircraft | |
| Fixed Wing | |
| Piper Navajo (4 Pass.) | 1 |
| Helicopters | |
| Bell 205 (14 Pass.) | 3 |
| Bell 206 (4 Pass.) | 1 |
| Bell 412 (14 Pass.) | 4 |
| *Total* | *9* |
| Buses | 2 |
| Cargo Vehicles | 10 |
| Command Van | 1 |
| Communications Trailer | 1 |
| Crew Carriers | 44 |
| Deluge Trucks | 2 |
| Dozer Tenders | 8 |
| Dozers | 7 |
| Dump Trucks | 11 |
| Engine Companies | 147 |
| Field Kitchens | 2 |
| Fire Boats | 2 |
| Foam Trucks | 2 |
| Foam Units | 3 |
| Food Dispensers | 6 |
| Fuel Dispensers | 2 |
| Graders | 3 |
| Hazardous Material Squads | 3 |
| Helicopter Tenders | 3 |
| Helicopter Utility Trucks | 2 |
| Hose Repair Truck | 1 |
| Hydroseeder | 1 |
| Infra-Red Van | 1 |

| | | |
|---|---|---|
| USAR | | 2 |
| Mobile Aid | | 1 |
| Mobile Air Utility | | 1 |
| Mobile Light Units | | 2 |
| Paramedic Units | | |
| Air Squads | 3 | |
| Engine Companies | 4 | |
| Rescue Squads | 51 | |
| *Total* | *58* | *268* |
| Patrol Fire Trucks | | 10 |
| Refrigerator Truck | | 1 |
| Repair Trucks | | 21 |
| Reserve Equipment | | |
| Crew Carriers | 13 | |
| Engine Companies | 42 | |
| Haz. Mat. Squad | 1 | |
| Repair Truck | 2 | |
| Rescue Squads | 15 | |
| Truck Companies | 4 | |
| *Total* | *77* | *32* |
| Salvage Truck | | 1 |
| Staff Vehicles | | 152 |
| Trailers | | 7 |
| Transports | | 7 |
| Traxcavator | | 2 |
| Truck Companies | | 24 |
| Utility Trucks | | 17 |
| Water Tenders | | 7 |
| Water Tower (50' Squirt) | | 4 |
| Watershed Pumpers | | 5 |
| *Total* | | *226* |
| **Total Equipment** | | **535** |

# APPARATUS LOCATOR INDEX
Listed by name of primary manufacturer